- Go to **awmi.net/sg425** to download PDFs of the following for each lesson in this workbook:
  - o Questions
  - o Additional Resources
- Share as many copies as you'd like.
- These documents are not for resale.

Sharper
than a
Two-Edged
Sword
Workbook

Summaries of Sixteen Foundational Teachings

Andrew Wommack

Sharper than a Two-Edged Sword Workbook
ISBN: 978-1-59548-177-1

Copyright © 2011 by Andrew Wommack Ministries Inc.
PO Box 3333
Colorado Springs CO 80934-3333

awmi.net

Topics

How to Use Your Workbook

Whether you are teaching a Sunday school class, leading a small group, discipling an individual, or studying on your own, this workbook is designed for you!

In our other study guides, the entire text of the corresponding book is included. However, because of the unique way *Sharper than a Two-Edged Sword* has been written, *CliffsNotes* style, the entire text of the book is not included in this workbook.

Each **Lesson** consists of **Questions, Answers**, and a list of **Additional Resources**.

For group study, begin each **Lesson** by having everyone read a chapter in Andrew's book *Sharper than a Two-Edged Sword*. Next, we recommend watching the As-Seen-on-TV DVD teaching on that subject (approximately thirty minutes long). Then go through the workbook **Lesson** together.

For personal study, read the chapter in the book. Next, we recommend watching the As-Seen-on-TV DVD teaching on that subject. Then answer the **Questions** and check your work with the **Answers**. For maximum impact, be sure to utilize the list of **Additional Resources**.

Outline for Group Study:
    I.   Read the current chapter aloud.
       A. Be sure that each student has a copy of the **Questions** and list of **Additional Resources**.
    II. Watch the corresponding DVD teaching.
    III. Afterward, facilitate a group Bible study using the **Questions** and **Answers**.

Materials Needed:
    Workbook, *Sharper than a Two-Edged Sword* book, *Sharper than a Two-Edged Sword* DVD teaching, Bible, and enough copies of the **Questions** and list of **Additional Resources** for each student. (PDFs of the **Questions** and **Additional Resources** can be downloaded via the URL located on the first page of this workbook.)

Outline for Personal Study:
    I.   Read the current chapter and watch the corresponding DVD teaching.
       A. Meditate on the given scriptures, as desired.
    II. Answer **Questions**.
    III. Check your work with the **Answers**.

Materials Needed:
    Workbook, *Sharper than a Two-Edged Sword* book, *Sharper than a Two-Edged Sword* DVD teaching, Bible, and a writing utensil.

True Christianity
Lesson 1

For God so loved the world, that he gave his only begotten Son, that whosoever believeth in him should not perish, but have everlasting life.

JOHN 3:16

"True Christianity teaches that we could never pay the debt we owe for sin, so God Himself became a man and paid the debt for us" (Sharper Than a Two-Edged Sword, Chapter 1).

1. Why should I believe that Jesus actually lived, or that He was anything more than a good man who taught with wisdom?

A. Jesus was a real man who lived on earth, and He claimed to be the Son of God. He said that only those who believed in Him could have eternal life. Either He was telling the truth, He was lying, or He was crazy. You can't just say Jesus was a good man. Either what Jesus said is true for everybody, or it isn't true for anybody.

Why should we believe that Jesus was telling the truth? For starters, liars and crazy people don't live the life of selflessness that Jesus lived. In fact, Jesus is the only truly selfless person who has ever lived. But there are many more reasons for us to believe He was telling the truth. Here are just a few:

Jesus performed innumerable miracles while He was on earth. Many of those miracles are recorded in Scripture (John 21:25) and also in accounts written by secular authors outside of the Bible (e.g., the Jewish historian Josephus). Jesus healed the sick, raised the dead, and gave sight to the blind. The miracles He performed are impossible without supernatural power. Countless miracles are still being performed today in the name of Jesus.

The Bible also contains over 300 prophecies about Jesus that were written 400 years or more before He was born, and He fulfilled them all. Many of them, He had no control over, such as the place He was born (Mic. 5:2), or how He would die (Is. 53 and Ps. 22): that His hands and feet would be pierced (Ps. 22:16), that soldiers would cast lots for His clothes (Ps 22:18), that He would be sold for thirty pieces of silver (Zech. 11:12 and Matt. 26:14-15), and that He would be buried with the rich (Is. 53:9 and Matt. 27:57-60).

Peter Stoner, author of *Science Speaks*, calculated the statistical probability of any one man fulfilling just 8 of those 300 prophecies. He determined that the odds are one in one hundred quadrillion! That is 1 in 100,000,000,000,000,000 (or 10^{17}).

Stoner illustrated the meaning of that number by stating that one hundred quadrillion silver dollars would completely cover the state of Texas two feet deep (an area larger than the countries of France and Austria combined). Mark one of those silver dollars, return it to the mass, and stir them all together. Then drop a man off somewhere in Texas, blindfold him, turn him out into the ocean of silver dollars, and have him bend down at random and select one coin. The odds of him picking up the marked silver dollar are the same as one man, by mere chance, fulfilling all eight of the prophecies Stoner selected.[1] *And Jesus fulfilled hundreds of prophecies, not a mere eight.*

We also know that God the Father testified that Jesus was His Son. He spoke from heaven in an audible voice that was heard by people standing around Jesus: **"This is my beloved Son, in whom I am well pleased"** (Matt. 3:17, 17:5; and 2 Pet. 1:17).

Not only have numerous people throughout history testified that Jesus is Lord, but many have given their lives for that belief! Church tradition states that all of Jesus' disciples, except John, were killed for telling others that Jesus is the Son of God. (They did try to boil John alive—it just didn't work. They couldn't kill him.) All the disciples had to do to save their lives was stop telling others about Jesus, but they refused. People don't endure hardship and suffering with joy, the way the disciples did, without a cause. The Apostle Peter denied even knowing Jesus when He was first arrested, but after Jesus rose from the dead, Peter spent his life preaching the good news that Jesus came to save us. Eventually, he was himself crucified for teaching about Jesus. (It's worth noting that Jesus appeared to over 500 believers after He rose from the dead [1 Cor. 15:6]).

The miracles Jesus performed, the prophecies He fulfilled, the testimony of God the Father, and the testimony of countless men and women throughout history all confirm that Jesus is exactly who He said He was: the Son of God.

Additionally, all of us know in our heart of hearts that God is real. He has revealed Himself to everyone who has ever been born (Rom. 1:18-20), and we all have an internal tugging that leads us to confront our need for God. A sense within tells us that God is real. Until we know Him, something feels like it is missing—we don't feel complete. Some people try to fill that void with success, wealth, possessions, busyness, and friends or spouses, but it doesn't go away. That hunger will only be satisfied by entering into a relationship with God.

---

1   *Science Speaks* by Peter Stoner Online Edition, Revision Nov. 2005, revised and HTML formatted, by Don W. Stoner. Available at www.sciencespeaks.dstoner.net/

Have you ever seen someone struggling with a task, but when you offered to help, you were refused? Like someone carrying four bags of groceries through a parking lot while trying to keep track of two children, rein in a dog on a leash, and have a conversation on a cell phone? That person might refuse your help, but that doesn't mean he or she doesn't need it. If you watch long enough, something is going to fall, run away, or break. Likewise, plenty of people in this world are busy denying that they need Jesus, but that doesn't mean they don't need Him.

The things that Jesus said are true for everyone, and one of the things Jesus said was **"Heaven and earth shall pass away: but my words shall not pass away"** (Mark 13:31). So, the things Jesus said are as true today as they were 2,000 years ago when He first said them.

Jesus is real, He is the Son of God, He is the only way to eternal life and relationship with God, and the words He spoke have direct implications for our lives and futures.

2. Why did God become a man and live on earth, and what does it mean for me?

A. When God created man, his spirit was alive because it was born of God, but the spirit of man died when he sinned. The Lord told Adam that in the day he ate the fruit of the Tree of the Knowledge of Good and Evil, he would surely die (Gen. 2:17). Adam and Eve lived for hundreds of years after they ate of the tree, so it wasn't physical death God was talking about. They died *spiritually* when they sinned, not physically.

Some people interpret the word "death" to mean ceasing to exist, but in reality people never cease to exist. The natural mind thinks of death as the end, but the Bible teaches that there is no end. Everyone lives forever; it's just a question of whether they exist for all eternity in the presence and joy of God or not.

Scripturally, death means separation. When Adam sinned, he died spiritually. His spirit didn't cease to exist, but it was separated from God. He no longer had the life of God inside of him. Sin caused a separation, and the spirit that was within him died. After sin entered the world, man was abandoned to his own wisdom. The very nature of man became dominated and controlled by the devil: it became lustful, selfish, and full of hatred and misery. The sin nature present in man means that hurt, pain, and negative influences don't originate from an outside source; they come from the inside.

After Adam and Eve sinned, they began to produce children, and they passed on their sin nature to every person who has ever been born of the flesh—

which excludes Jesus. Jesus was born of a virgin (Is. 7:14 and Matt. 1:23). He didn't get His life through man. He received a physical body through a woman, but His life came directly from God. So, with the exception of Jesus, every person who has ever been born on this earth has been born into sin with a nature that is corrupted and separated from God.

Man's separation from God isn't about individual actions, or sins; acts of sin are a result of the sin nature. A child doesn't have to be taught to do evil; he or she will do it naturally. The sins we commit don't give us a sin nature; it's the other way around: The sin nature we were born with drives us to do evil.

Sin was a barrier that stood between humanity and God, so God became a man to remove that barrier and restore us to intimate relationship with Him. Jesus Christ was God in the flesh, and He lived a sinless life. He earned relationship with God through His own goodness. Although Jesus had done no wrong, He was killed on the cross and suffered for our sins. He took our punishment. He sacrificed Himself for us. God's anger against sin fell upon Jesus, and He forever satisfied the wrath of God against the sin of the human race. Jesus has paid for *all* sin for *all* time, and because of that, you and I can have eternal life—not by being good, not by earning it ourselves, but simply by receiving the salvation Jesus paid for.

There is only one sin that separates you from God, and that is failing to believe in Jesus (John 16:7-9). Salvation comes down to one thing: Will you accept what Jesus has done for you?

3. **What if I want to believe something different? Can't I follow another religion and still meet with God in the afterlife, as long as I'm a good person?**

   A.   Salvation and eternal life are all about Jesus. Some people try to say Jesus was a great example of love, but that He is only one way to God. Jesus isn't *a* way; He is the *only way* to the Father.

   The Bible says, **"Neither is there salvation in any other: for there is none other name under heaven given among men, whereby we must be saved"** (Acts 4:12).

   Jesus also said of Himself, **"I am the way, the truth, and the life: no man cometh unto the Father, but by me"** (John 14:6). Jesus proclaimed that He was absolutely the only way.

   If you try to stand before God in your own goodness, you are going to come up short. All of us have sinned and fall short of the glory of God (Rom. 3:23). The only thing that will make you worthy to receive everlasting life is the payment Jesus made for your sins, and you claiming Him to be your Lord and Savior. You have to put your faith in the goodness of God through Jesus.

Everyone who trusts in Jesus will be made in right standing with God. Those attempting to trust in their own goodness will never be able to live up to God's standard of perfection. The only way to have relationship with God is to have it through faith in Jesus.

4. Why do I have to be born again to see the kingdom of God? And what does it mean to be born again?

    A.   Jesus said, **"Verily, verily, I say unto thee, Except a man be born again, he cannot see the kingdom of God"** (John 3:3). Jesus went on to reiterate the need to be born again by saying, **"Verily, verily, I say unto thee, Except a man be born of water and of the Spirit, he cannot enter into the kingdom of God"** (John 3:5).

Some debate the meaning of being **"born of water,"** but I believe it is simply a reference to natural birth. A woman about to give birth is said to have her "water break," meaning that the amniotic fluid that surrounds a baby in the womb has dispersed in preparation for childbirth. Jesus was saying that unless you have a natural birth—when you were born in water—and then the second birth when you are born of the Spirit of God, you cannot enter into the kingdom of God.

The second birth is what we call being "born again." So, just as surely as people have to be born physically to exist in this world, you have to be born again of the Spirit to enter into the kingdom of God.

I grew upgoing to church, and I tried to be a good Christian, but I just couldn't do it. A couple of times in my life, I've gone back and tried again, but I always fail. I don't think God wants anything to do with me anymore. Is that true?

Every other major religion, and even a large portion of what is called Christianity, is preaching that you have to earn relationship with God by being good. I'm making a distinction here because not everyone who claims to be a Christian is a true Christian. True Christianity teaches that we could never pay the debt we owe for sin, so God Himself became a man and paid the debt for us.

Relationship with God is something you receive; it isn't something you earn. When you accept Jesus, you get changed on the inside, you are born again from above. Now, true Christianity does preach that you should live a good life, but a good life isn't the root of your relationship with God—it's the *fruit* of relationship with Him. You start living holy as a result of having a relationship with God, not as a means of obtaining it. Those are subtle distinctions, but the difference is profound. It is what divides true Christianity from every other religion in this world.

If you have a desire to know God, that desire is coming from Him. It means God is still dealing with you and drawing you into a relationship with Him. It doesn't matter how many times you have failed in the past. Draw near to God, and He will draw near to you (James 4:8).

5. Is being born again just about getting into heaven when I die, or is there more?

A. Being born again is about more than just getting into heaven when you die. Jesus died to give you eternal life, and eternal life is relationship with God—relationship that begins the moment you are born again (John 17:3). After you are born again, it is essential that you learn your new identity in Christ so you can walk in victory and fulfill the plans God has for your life.

God desires to pour out His blessings upon you, but you have to know how to cooperate with Him to receive all that He has for you. The remainder of this **Workbook** will teach you about your new identity in Christ and how to cooperate with Him in your new life.

6. What do I need to do to be born again?

A. The Bible says that if you confess with your mouth that Jesus is Lord and you believe in your heart that God raised Him from the dead, you will be saved (Rom. 10:9).

Notice that it has to be more than an internal decision. Jesus said that whoever confesses Him before others, He will confess before the Father, but whoever denies Him before others, He will deny before the Father (Matt. 10:32-33). Receiving salvation has to be real enough that you live it and share it with other people.

Choosing to receive Jesus as your Savior and be born again from above is the most important decision you will ever make. Everything that is seen in this world is going to pass away, but those who know Jesus as Lord will never die (John 11:25-26). If you have come to realize what true salvation is and you're ready to receive it, then say this prayer out loud and you will be born again. It's that simple.

Father, I'm sorry for my sins. I believe Jesus died to forgive my sin, and I receive that forgiveness. Jesus, I make You my Lord. I believe that You are alive and that You now live in me. I am saved. I am forgiven. Thank You, Jesus!

If you said that prayer and believed it in your heart, then you are born again! You might look the same on the outside, but you are a whole new person. Your spirit is now alive with the life of God. You have been set free from the powers of darkness and delivered into the kingdom of God's dear Son (Col. 1:13).

Additional Resources:

1. *The New You* is a two-part audio teaching available to listen to or download for free at www.awmi.net/extra/audio/1039.

2. *The New You & The Holy Spirit* is a book by Andrew Wommack that covers what happened when you received Jesus as your Savior, and it details how the Holy Spirit is the key to living the abundant life that Jesus provided through His death and resurrection. It is available through the online store at www.awmi.net/store/usa/books/323.

3. "Eternal Life" is an audio teaching available to listen to or download for free at www.awmi.net/extra/audio/general.

4. *Effortless Change* is a book by Andrew Wommack that reveals how the power of God's Word effects effortless change. It is available through the online store at www.awmi.net/store/usa/books/331.

5. *A Sure Foundation* is a summary of the first four teachings Andrew gives at Charis Bible College in Colorado. It is a four-part audio teaching available to listen to or download for free at www.awmi.net/extra/audio/1034.

The Holy Spirit
Lesson 2

And I will pray the Father, and he shall give you another Comforter, that he may abide with you for ever.

JOHN 14:16

"We need the power of the Holy Spirit living in us, inspiring us, and anointing the words we speak" (Sharper Than a Two-Edged Sword, Chapter 2).

1. How is the Holy Spirit going to help me live the Christian life?

A. Being a Christian isn't hard for us to do on our own—it is impossible. God never intended for us to try to live godly lives without His power and support. The Holy Spirit is the One who empowers us to live the Christian life, and we can't do it without Him.

Also, the Word of God is a spiritual book written under the inspiration of the Holy Spirit, and we need the Holy Spirit to understand it (2 Tim. 3:16-17). It isn't enough to know in your mind what the Bible says; you have to understand it in your heart. The Word says, **"But the natural man receiveth not the things of the Spirit of God: for they are foolishness unto him: neither can he know them, because they are spiritually discerned"** (1 Cor. 2:14). God wrote the Bible to our hearts, not to our heads, and we can't comprehend the things of God with our human intellect. The Word of God is the truth that will set you free, but you need the Holy Spirit to make the Word come alive as you read it in order to get understanding.

2. Why did Jesus tell His disciples not to do anything until they received the Holy Spirit?

A. After Jesus rose from the dead, He met with His disciples to give them some last-minute instruction before He turned over the future of His kingdom to them. They were going to be responsible for telling the world the good news and presenting God's plan of salvation. He was about to put everything He had worked and suffered for into their hands.

Jesus' last words to them were certainly important. He said, **"But ye shall receive power, after that the Holy Ghost is come upon you: and**

ye shall be witnesses unto me both in Jerusalem, and in all Judaea, and in Samaria, and unto the uttermost part of the earth" (Acts 1:8).

Jesus didn't want the disciples out there trying to advance His kingdom in their own strength, because He knew that they would fail. We can't be effective witnesses for Christ without the Holy Spirit.

3. What is the difference between being born again and the baptism of the Holy Spirit?

A. The baptism of the Holy Spirit is a separate experience from salvation. It is a second encounter with God, when you receive power from on high. Jesus Himself didn't begin His public ministry until He received an anointing from the Holy Spirit—even though He was God from birth. He was born God, yet He didn't begin His ministry until He received the Holy Spirit (Matt. 3:16-17). The Bible doesn't mention a single miracle in His life until after that time. If Jesus needed the power of the Holy Spirit before He began to minister and if He told His disciples not to minister without the power of the Holy Spirit, then it would be arrogant for us to believe we can accomplish anything in our own power.

Additionally, the book of Acts gives several scriptural examples that prove the baptism of the Holy Spirit is a separate experience from being born again. In one instance, Philip preached in the city of Samaria, and the entire city believed in Jesus (Acts 8:4-8). During that time, Philip performed many miracles, and there was great revival in that city. But then it says,

> **Now when the apostles which were at Jerusalem heard that Samaria had received the word of God, they sent unto them Peter and John: Who, when they were come down, prayed for them, that they might receive the Holy Ghost: (For as yet he was fallen upon none of them: only they were baptized in the name of the Lord Jesus.) Then laid they their hands on them, and they received the Holy Ghost.**
>
> **ACTS 8:14-17**

This scripture makes it clear that the Samarians were born again. Then they were baptized in water. Philip wouldn't have baptized them unless they had already believed and were converted. Clearly, these people were born again. So, they were already Christians, but they had not yet received the Holy Spirit. The apostles went down to their city and prayed for them to receive the Holy Spirit *after* their initial born-again experience.

This same thing is recorded when the Apostle Paul found some people who were already disciples but were not filled with the Holy Spirit (Acts 19:1-7). When Paul asked them if they had received the Holy Spirit since they believed, they said, "We haven't even heard there is a Holy Spirit." Paul prayed for those men, and they received the Holy Spirit and spoke in tongues.

Another scriptural example is given from the ministry of Jesus. Following His death and resurrection, Jesus appeared to His disciples on several occasions. The first time He appeared to them, one of the disciples, Thomas, was not present. The other disciples told Thomas that Jesus had risen from the dead, but Thomas didn't believe them. He said, **"Except I shall see in his hands the print of the nails, and put my finger into the print of the nails, and thrust my hand into his side, I will not believe"** (John 20:25).

Eight days later, all of the disciples were gathered together, and Thomas was with them. Jesus appeared in the midst of them and said to Thomas, **"Reach hither thy finger, and behold my hands; and reach hither thy hand, and thrust it into my side: and be not faithless, but believing"** (John 20:27). Jesus then commented that Thomas believed because he saw but blessed are those who have not seen and yet believe. Upon hearing this, Thomas answered Jesus and said, **"My Lord and my God"** (John 20:28).

We know from Scripture that all it takes to be born again is to confess with your mouth that Jesus is Lord and believe in your heart that God raised Him from the dead (Rom. 10:9-10). Thomas confessed that Jesus is Lord, and Jesus commented that he believed it, so we can conclude that Thomas must have been born again. Yet Thomas was one of the eleven disciples that Jesus told to wait until the Holy Spirit was given, so being born again and receiving the Holy Spirit can't be the same experience.

I have heard people try to get around these scriptures by claiming that this was a special circumstance because the Holy Spirit hadn't been given to anyone yet. Now, they contend, people receive all of the power and presence of the Holy Spirit available when they are born again. But the book of Acts is full of examples showing that the born-again experience and the baptism of the Holy Spirit remained separate experiences long after the Day of Pentecost.

4. Are you saying I didn't get all of the Holy Spirit's ability when I was born again?

A. You get the Holy Spirit when you are born again, because you have to have the Spirit of God in you in order to be born again (1 Cor. 12:3). When you are born again, you become a temple of the Holy Spirit (1 Cor. 6:19). So, people who don't speak in tongues aren't any less saved than those who do, and God doesn't love those who speak in tongues any more than those who don't. But there is more of the Holy Spirit to experience than being born again, and the baptism of the Holy Spirit is about more than just speaking in tongues.

The night before Jesus was crucified, He taught and prepared the disciples for what was coming. One of the things Jesus told them was, **"And I will pray the Father, and he shall give you another Comforter, that he may abide with you for ever"** (John 14:16). The Comforter is the Holy Spirit.

The Greek language has two different words for "another." One means "another of the same sort," and the other word means "another of a different sort" (*Vine's Expository Dictionary of Old and New Testament Words*). Jesus said He was going to send another of the same sort—another One, the Comforter, just like Himself. He was telling the disciples not to worry about His departure, because He was going to send the Holy Spirit to continue His ministry on earth and to continue doing all the things He had been doing.

After Jesus went to the Father, it became possible for the Holy Spirit to reside in born-again believers and to operate through us. Instead of only working through Jesus, the Holy Spirit can now operate through as many as believe in Jesus—**but we have to cooperate with Him**. The Holy Spirit isn't going to force Himself upon us, just as Jesus doesn't force salvation upon us. We have to make a choice to submit to Him. **And we can't cooperate with the Holy Spirit if we refuse to recognize His presence and ability in us.**

Ask yourself this question: If God could give you more power and ability to live the Christian life and to help other people, would you want it? The baptism of the Holy Spirit is simply an act of recognizing, acknowledging, and welcoming the Holy Spirit and His work, power, and presence in your life. It's saying "yes" to Him and letting Him know you want to cooperate with Him.

You don't *have* to be baptized in the Holy Spirit; you *get* to be baptized in the Holy Spirit. It is an enormous privilege, and it will empower you to live a life you never imagined possible.

5. What does "speaking in tongues" mean?

A. Speaking in tongues is a manifestation of the Holy Spirit's power in us after we have received the baptism of the Holy Spirit. It is when the Holy Spirit inspires our spirits to pray to God, using the same vocal chords we use to speak but making sounds that our natural minds can't understand (1 Cor. 14:2). It's our spirits speaking to God by the power of the Holy Spirit.

There are about a dozen instances recorded in the book of Acts when people received the baptism of the Holy Spirit, and in every instance, they spoke in tongues. They didn't speak in tongues some of the time or most of the time; they spoke in tongues *every* time.

6. **Why should I speak in tongues? What is it going to do for me?**

    A. Without the baptism of the Holy Spirit and speaking in tongues, you can't live the life that God intends for you to live. It is the power to live the Christian life. I guarantee that the baptism of the Holy Spirit and speaking in tongues will produce a radical change in your relationship with God. The Word of God will come alive, and you will begin to see and understand things you never noticed before. You need this ability.

    Speaking in tongues builds your faith (Jude 20). It also helps to draw out into your natural mind the wisdom that is in your spirit. Your spirit contains the mind of Christ (1 Cor. 2:16) and knows all things (1 John 2:20). Speaking in tongues draws that knowledge out and will enable you to know things that you couldn't possibly know with your natural mind—for example, facts about a person's life, future events, and wisdom in making decisions. Speaking in tongues will also bring you supernatural rest and refreshing (Is. 28:11-12) and will enable you to give thanks to God beyond the limits of human language (1 Cor. 14:15-17).

7. **Is God still giving believers the gift of speaking in tongues today?**

    A. Speaking in tongues is a valid gift for today, and it accompanies receiving the baptism of the Holy Spirit. If you don't speak in tongues, then your beliefs are preventing you from doing so, or you haven't received the baptism of the Holy Spirit.

    I received the Holy Spirit about ten years after I was born again, but it took me another three years to speak in tongues. I wanted to speak in tongues, I prayed for it, but I had been taught so much against speaking in tongues that I couldn't do it. I had too much fear and unbelief built up in me. It took me a while to get my mind renewed by the Word of God and to get rid of the unbelief.

    I'm mentioning this to show that it is possible to be born again and to have had an encounter with the Holy Spirit, yet not speak in tongues. If you have had an encounter with the Holy Spirit but you don't speak in tongues, it's because you've been taught something that is hindering you. The ability to pray in tongues is important in the life of believers, and it is a gift from God we need today.

8. **I still have a lot of problems that I'm struggling with. Why would God want to give me the ability of speaking in tongues? I don't feel worthy.**

    A. God wants you to have the baptism of the Holy Spirit and to speak in tongues even more than you do. Jesus said,

If a son shall ask bread of any of you that is a father, will he give him a stone? or if he ask a fish, will he for a fish give him a serpent? Or if he shall ask an egg, will he offer him a scorpion? If ye then, being evil, know how to give good gifts unto your children: how much more shall your heavenly Father give the Holy Spirit to them that ask him?

LUKE 11:11-13

Some people teach that you can't have any sin in your life or else God won't fill you with the Holy Spirit. They think that God won't fill a dirty vessel. *I want you to know that God doesn't have any other kind of vessel to fill!* If you could be perfect without the Holy Spirit, you wouldn't need Him. The very fact that you aren't perfect makes you a candidate to be filled with the Holy Spirit. It is God's will for every born-again believer to be filled with the Holy Spirit and to speak in tongues. He created you to fill with His Spirit, so there is no way He won't do it when you ask.

9. How does speaking in tongues work?

A. One of the things that kept me from speaking in tongues right away when I was baptized in the Holy Spirit was that I didn't understand that I had to do the speaking. The Holy Spirit inspires you, but *you* have to do the talking. The Bible says, **"And they were all filled with the Holy Ghost, and began to speak with other tongues, as the Spirit gave them utterance"** (Acts 2:4).

Just as God doesn't make people receive salvation, He isn't going to *make* you speak in tongues. God doesn't take over people's bodies—it's going to be your voice, and you have to start and stop. You can't just open your mouth and wait for sound to come out.

As you begin to utter the words the Holy Spirit is inspiring you to speak, the words will come more and more easily. You won't understand what you are saying, because the natural mind can't understand the things of the spirit (1 Cor. 2:14), but you can pray for an interpretation (1 Cor. 14:13).

Getting an interpretation doesn't mean you'll get a word-for-word translation of everything you have said in tongues. It could mean that you'll pray in tongues today, and sometime in the near future, God will give you a word of knowledge or wisdom. The only time that an interpretation is required immediately is when someone speaks in tongues during a church service. It isn't necessary when you are praying in tongues privately.

10. What do I need to do to be baptized in the Holy Spirit?

A. The only requirement for receiving the Holy Spirit is to be born again. Jesus is the one who baptizes in the Holy Spirit (Matt. 3:11), so if you haven't received the Giver, you can't receive the gift.

If you recognize that you need this gift, all you have to do is ask God, and He will give it to you:

Father, I thank You that I am the temple of the Holy Spirit. Holy Spirit, I welcome You to fill me right now. Thank You for filling me with Your presence.

Sometimes people feel something when they are filled with the Holy Spirit, and sometimes not. When I received the Holy Spirit, I didn't feel a thing, but I got Him. Regardless of whether or not you felt anything, begin to speak in tongues by faith. Open your mouth and utter the words that the Holy Spirit is inspiring within you.

Make praying in tongues a regular practice, and you will begin to see the supernatural power of God manifesting in your life!

Additional Resources:

1. *The Holy Spirit* is a two-part audio teaching available to listen to or download for free at www.awmi.net/extra/audio/1040.

2. *The New You & The Holy Spirit* is a book by Andrew Wommack that covers what happened when you received Jesus as your Savior and how the Holy Spirit is the key to living the abundant life that Jesus provided through His death and resurrection. It is available through the online store at www.awmi.net/store/usa/books/323.

3. *The Positive Ministry of the Holy Spirit* is a four-part audio teaching available to listen to or download for free at www.awmi.net/extra/audio/1020.

4. *How to Hear God's Voice* is a three-part audio teaching. Hearing the voice of the Lord is probably the single most important element in having a victorious Christian life after being born again. This series is available to listen to or download for free at www.awmi.net/extra/audio/1030.

5. *How to Flow in the Gifts of the Holy Spirit* is a three-part audio teaching available to listen to or download for free at www.awmi.net/extra/audio/1031.

Spirit, Soul & Body
Lesson 3

And the very God of peace sanctify you wholly; and I pray God your whole spirit and soul and body be preserved blameless unto the coming of our Lord Jesus Christ.

1 THESSALONIANS 5:23

"The Christian life boils down to this simple truth: In your spirit, you are as saved as you'll ever be. You're as holy and righteous as Jesus is. You have His faith, His power, and His anointing" (Sharper Than a Two-Edged Sword, Chapter 3).

1. **Which part of me becomes new when I am born again?**

   A. Every human being consists of three parts: a spirit, a soul, and a body Functionally, most people only acknowledge the body and the soul. The body is obvious. We can see our bodies, and all of us are aware of what our bodies look like. We know whether we are male or female, tall or short. We also know there is an inner part of us that isn't physical. We know that words don't touch us physically, but they touch our hearts and can cause joy, pain, and other emotions. That's the soul.

      Every person instinctively understands that they have a body and a soul because they are aware of those two characteristics, but the third part cannot be sensed—the spirit. *The spirit is the part of man that is born again, and understanding this is the key to a fruitful relationship with God.*

2. **What happens in my spirit when I am born again?**

   A. The Bible says, **"Therefore if any man be in Christ, he is a new creature: old things are passed away; behold, all things are become new"** (2 Cor. 5:17).

      After you are born again, you become a completely new creation. Clearly, it isn't your body that changes. If you were a woman before you got saved, you're still going to be a woman afterward. Tall, short, fat, or skinny, the body doesn't change when you are born again. Neither does the soul become completely new. Personality traits can change over time, but they aren't instantly transformed when you are saved. In order for emotional and personality traits to change, you have to renew your mind.

Second Corinthians 5:17 doesn't say you will be a new creation someday or that you are in the process of becoming one—it says you *are* a new creation. It also says that *all* things are new, not some things. The total change spoken of here cannot be observed in your body or soul (the mental, emotional part of you). In fact, it can't be outwardly observed at all, because the transformation takes place in your spirit, where you can't feel a thing.

It is your spirit that becomes a completely brand-new work of God when you are born again. Your body and soul are being influenced by your born-again spirit, but they are only in the process of changing. In the spirit, you are a completely brand-new creation. You are a new species of being that never existed before (2 Cor. 5:17).

3. Is my spirit affected by the sin nature?

A. If you are born again, your spirit is as pure, as righteous, and as holy as it will ever be in eternity. Your spirit is perfect: it contains no sin, no inadequacy, no fear, no depression, and no discouragement. There is nothing negative in your spirit. Your born-again spirit is identical to Jesus! I know some people balk at that, but it's what the Word says:

> **Herein is our love made perfect, that we may have boldness in the day of judgment: because as He is, so are we in this world.**
>
> **1 JOHN 4:17**

This isn't a promise that we are going to be like Jesus in heaven; it says we are, *in this world*, just as He is. There is no way to understand that verse if we are thinking only of the body and the soul, because neither of them is identical to Jesus. Our bodies and souls are in the process of change, but the completion of that process won't take place until we are caught up with the Lord. The only way to understand that we are, *right now*, just as Jesus is, is to realize that it is our spirits that have become new creations. Our spirits have already changed, and one-third of our salvation is complete.

When we die and go to be with the Lord, or if the Lord comes back first and we receive glorified bodies, our bodies are going to be changed. Our minds will be changed. But right now, our spirits are identical to the way they will be in eternity. They're identical to Jesus. As Jesus is, that's the way that we are.

4. If nothing can damage my born-again spirit, then why can't I just live however I want to and not worry about it? Won't God still love me?

A. God isn't dealing with us based upon our sin and failure in the flesh; He is relating to us through our spirits, which are new creations. In the spirit, we are created in righteousness and true holiness (Eph. 4:24). We don't have to go out and try to earn holiness or beg God to send it down from heaven. And, once our spirits are born again, they are sealed by the power of the Holy Spirit for protection (Eph. 1:13). A barrier is formed to keep sin out and to maintain the purity of our born-again spirits. So, committing sin doesn't alter the righteousness of our born-again spirits, and it doesn't change the way God loves us. But living in sin is dumb.

The Scripture says, **"Know ye not, that to whom ye yield yourselves servants to obey, his servants ye are to whom ye obey; whether of sin unto death, or of obedience unto righteousness?"** (Rom. 6:16). When you live in sin, you are making yourself a servant of the devil, and you are giving him permission to come into your life and wreak havoc. Giving Satan access to you like that is stupid because he only comes into your life to steal, kill, and destroy (John 10:10). God will still love you, but sin isn't smart. It will harden your heart and prevent you from loving God and fully benefiting from His blessing upon your life.

5. What does "renewing my mind" mean?

A. The mind is an influential force in your life. The Word says that as a man thinks in his heart, that's the way he is going to be (Prov. 23:7). It doesn't matter what encounters you have with the Lord; the way you think will ultimately be the way your life goes. This is one of the greatest truths in the Bible, and it is important to understand.

The way you think isn't instantly renewed when you are born again. You can't have someone wave a hand over you and transform your mind. Even though experiences can have an impact on you, they don't necessarily change what you believe. Thought is a systematic process, and you have to renew your mind. You have to change the way you think. The Bible says,

> **And be not conformed to this world: but be ye transformed by the renewing of your mind, that ye may prove what is that good, and acceptable, and perfect, will of God.**
>
> **ROMANS 12:2**

The word **"transformed"** comes from the same Greek word from which we get *metamorphosis*, which is the process whereby a caterpillar spins a cocoon and later emerges as a butterfly. If you want to transform from something that is earthbound to something that is beautiful and able to fly, it comes through the renewing of your mind.

As a believer, you have to renew your mind to avoid being conformed to the patterns of this world. Unless you renew your mind, the wrong patterns of thinking you have developed in life are eventually going to choke out the fruit that God is trying to produce in you. Renewing your mind is the process of reprogramming your mind through the Word of God to see life from God's perspective.

6. You say I'm as righteous as Jesus, but I can't believe that. It's not possible—if my spirit was identical to Jesus, I'd know it! Wouldn't I?

A. If I ask you whether you are feeling any pain in your body, you don't have to pray about it and get back to me. You know when you are feeling pain. In the same way, if I ask you how you are feeling emotionally, you can tell me: happy or sad, depressed or encouraged. You are constantly monitoring your body and your soul, so you intuitively understand those two aspects of your identity. According to Scripture, however, you are three parts—not two. You have a body, a soul, *and* a spirit. But unlike the body and the soul, the spirit part can't be sensed.

Understanding that your spirit truly is identical to Jesus will change your life. Until I understood that my spirit was made new, I looked at faults in my thinking or behavior and couldn't understand how God could love me. I experienced God's love, but I was looking at all of my shortcomings. I didn't always act right or say the right thing, and I couldn't comprehend how God Almighty could love me or use me. The problem was that I was looking at the flesh, but God was looking at my spirit. God accepts you based on what He did in your born-again spirit, not based on what you do.

7. If I have the power and faith of Jesus in my spirit, then why do I need to bother renewing my mind?

A. The Christian life boils down to this simple truth: In your spirit, you are as saved as you'll ever be. You're as holy and righteous as Jesus is. You have His faith, His power, and His anointing. All you have to do is renew your mind, and the way you do that is by reading the Word of God and believing what it says about you. It's only the truth you know that sets you free (John 8:32), so you have to meditate on the Word until you know your spiritual identity.

The mind is like a valve to the spirit and the life of God that it contains: It has the power to release or to obstruct the power of God in your life. A mind that is focused on what is going on in the body and soul will shut off the power of God. It forms a two-against-one majority with the flesh, and even though you have the life of God in your spirit, you won't experience it. Getting your mind into agreement with your spirit, on the other hand, opens up the flow of God's power.

We can't afford to shut off God's power in our lives. We have to renew our minds to the truth contained in God's Word and come into agreement with God's view of who we are. Our spirits are already perfect. When our minds align with our spirits, we'll begin to see the ability of God that is in our spirits spill over into our bodies and souls. Our bodies will get healed, our emotions will be healed, and we'll see the anointing of God pour out into our lives.

8. How is the Word of God relevant to my daily life?

A. The Apostle Peter was with Jesus on the Mount of Transfiguration when God the Father spoke in an audible voice from heaven and said, **"This is my beloved Son, in whom I am well pleased"** (Matt. 17:5). But Peter considered Scripture even better than hearing the audible voice of God. He said, **"We have also a more sure word of prophecy; whereunto ye do well that ye take heed, as unto a light that shineth in a dark place, until the day dawn, and the day star arise in your hearts"** (2 Pet. 1:19).

The Bible was written for our instruction. It is a lamp to guide our feet, and a light to help find our path through life (Ps. 119:105). It contains wisdom for our daily lives, and we have to know the truth revealed in the Word in order to discern God's leading. If we don't know what God says in His Word, we'll be susceptible to being deceived by false teachers and false doctrine.

The Word of God is the primary method God uses to speak to believers. God has given us knowledge of His promises in the Word so we can partake of His divine nature in this life. The single most important aspect of the Christian life is spending time with God by meditating on His Word and renewing our minds.

9. How should I go about reading my Bible?

A. Read the Bible systematically, but don't start in Genesis and read straight through to Revelation. The New Testament contains the revelation of Jesus as the fulfillment of God's plan of redemption for mankind, and believers should start there. After you have read and understood the New Testament, then you can go back and properly understand the events of the Old Testament.

Read the Word slowly and expectantly, knowing that the Word of God is alive and active and that God desires to reveal mysteries to you through it (Heb. 4:12).

Additional Resources:

1. *Spirit, Soul & Body* is a four-part audio teaching available to listen to or download for free at www.awmi.net/extra/audio/1027.

2. *Spirit, Soul & Body*, the book by Andrew Wommack, **contains the foundational revelation to everything Andrew teaches**. If you have trouble receiving from God, this is a must-read! It is available at www.awmi.net/store/usa/books/318.

3. "Who You Are in the Spirit" is an audio teaching available to listen to or download for free at www.awmi.net/extra/audio/righteousness.

You've Already Got It!
Lesson 4

Now faith is the substance of things hoped for, the evidence of things not seen.

HEBREWS 11:1

"Whatever you are asking God to give you has already been provided. You don't need to get God to heal, save, deliver, or prosper you, or to give you joy and peace. All of those things have already been supplied" (Sharper than a Two-Edged Sword, Chapter 4).

1. **If God has already given me everything I need, then where is it?**

    A. It's in your spirit. You can't feel by sensation what is in your spirit. By contrast, your body instantly knows whether you have pain or feel good. In the same way, your soul is constantly monitoring how you feel emotionally: whether happy, mad, hurt, or sad, you know it. Because you always know what is going on in your body and soul, you may assume that if you had the healing power of God in your spirit you would know it. But you can't feel what you have in your spirit. The only way you can discern what is true in the spirit is through the Word of God.

    Jesus said, **"The words that I speak unto you, they are spirit, and they are life"** (John 6:63). God's Word is like a spiritual mirror: If you want to know what you have in your spirit, you have to look into the Word of God to see what it says.

2. **What does the "substance" of what I'm hoping for mean, and what does the "evidence" of things I can't see mean? Can you give me a practical example?**

    A. In the *King James Version*, Hebrews 11:1 defines faith as **"the substance of things hoped for, the evidence of things not seen."** Viewing how other Bible translations have rendered this passage might help you gain a better understanding.

    The *Amplified Bible, Classic Edition* says, **"Now faith is the assurance (the confirmation, the title deed) of the things [we] hope for, being the proof of things [we] do not see and the conviction of their reality [faith perceiving as real fact what is not revealed to the senses]."**

The *New Living Translation* reads, **"Faith is the confidence that what we hope for will actually happen; it gives us assurance about things we cannot see."**

Faith acts like a bridge that runs from the spirit realm over into the physical realm, allowing what is in the spirit to cross over into manifestation. Or you could say that faith is like a pipe through which all that God has provided in the spirit flows into the physical realm. If you don't have that bridge, or conduit, of faith, you probably won't see God's power manifest in your life. It isn't that God hasn't given; it's that your lack of faith is shutting off the flow of His power.

Understanding that you already have God's power in your spirit will greatly increase the degree of His provision that you experience in life. God has placed Himself on the inside of you. In your spirit, you already have healing, prosperity, joy, peace, deliverance, love, and anything else you could ever need. Before a need arises, God has anticipated it, and His supply is greater than any need. No problem or obstacle can come your way that God hasn't made provision for. He has given you the power and wisdom to deal with whatever circumstances come along. You just have to believe that God has already released His power and made provision for you—even when there is no physical evidence to support that fact.

3. **I know God has already paid for my sins, but what about the ones I haven't even committed yet?**

   A. Jesus Christ made *one* sacrifice for all sin, for all time. God has already dealt with every sin you have ever committed or will commit in the future. Forgiveness has already been provided. This point is stressed emphatically in the book of Hebrews:

   > **By the which will we are sanctified through the offering of the body of Jesus Christ once for all.**
   >
   > **HEBREWS 10:10**

   > **But this man, after he had offered one sacrifice for sins forever, sat down on the right hand of God.**
   >
   > **HEBREWS 10:12**

   > **Neither by the blood of goats and calves, but by his own blood he entered in once into the holy place, having obtained eternal redemption for us.**
   >
   > **HEBREWS 9:12**

Jesus paid for your sins and reconciled you to God, and everything you will ever need has already been provided through Him. God has already paid for all of your sins—including the ones you haven't committed yet.

4. How can I already have healing if my body is sick?

    A. The Scripture says, **"Who his own self bare our sins in his own body on the tree, that we, being dead to sins, should live unto righteousness: by whose stripes ye were healed"** (1 Pet. 2:24).

        In this scripture, the Apostle Peter said Jesus fulfilled the prophecy of healing written in the book of Isaiah (Is. 53:4-5). The Gospel of Matthew also quotes the same verses to show that Jesus provided for the healing of our physical bodies (Matt. 8:16-17).

        Notice that 1 Peter 2:24 says you *were* healed by Jesus' stripes. When was it that Jesus took stripes on His body? It was during His ministry, when He was mocked by the soldiers, beaten, and then led away to be crucified. It was 2,000 years ago that Jesus bore stripes, and by His stripes, we *were* healed! Jesus has already provided healing. He isn't up in heaven having stripes put on His back right now.

        Christians, as a whole, know that God has the power to perform miracles. They believe He *can* do anything, so they don't have a problem believing that God is capable of meeting their needs. The question people have is "*Will* God do it?"

        I don't understand everything about how healing works, but I know that God's Word clearly states He has already provided healing to everyone who will believe. All things are possible for those who believe (Mark 9:23), and if people can believe that God has already healed them, then God's healing power will come through their spirits, into their bodies, and make them well again.

    B. This topic is more thoroughly discussed during the **Lessons** "The Believer's Authority" and "God Wants You Well."

5. What is the advantage to already having healing, prosperity, etc., in my spirit versus just asking God to give them to me when I am in need?

    A. It is far easier to release something you already have than it is to try to obtain something you don't have.

        It's a step in the right direction to believe that God *can* heal, but there is still an element of doubt in that approach. It's the equivalent of looking at something way off in the future—"It might happen, but then again, it might not." When you begin to understand that *you already have healing*, it's a whole different story. The healing might not have manifested in your body yet, but you will know, by faith, that you already have healing in your spirit.

God's power, the same power that raised Jesus from the dead, is already on the inside of you (Eph. 1:3 and 19-20). You don't have to pray and ask God to come heal you; you've already got it! You already have prosperity. You already have anointing. You already have wisdom. You already have faith. On and on it goes. It is all in your spirit.

The Apostle Paul said that faith works by **"the acknowledging of every good thing which is in you in Christ Jesus"** (Philem. 6)—not by asking God to give you something you already have. Faith works by simply acknowledging, or getting a revelation of, what is already in you. And faith is the conduit through which God's power flows into our lives.

6. Why can't I feel how much God loves me all of the time?

A. God's love is in your spirit, and you can't feel, or sense, what you have in your spirit. The only way you can discern what is true in the spirit is through the Word of God. The Bible says, **"But God commendeth his love toward us, in that, while we were yet sinners, Christ died for us"** (Rom. 5:8).

God's love for us is without question. There is nothing we can do that will make Him love us more than He already does. The problem people have is that they don't necessarily *feel* God's love. But we can't go by our feelings. Feelings are tied to the flesh, not our spirits. As believers, it is important for us to walk in the Spirit, not in the flesh (Gal. 5:16 and 25). We have to believe what God says above how we feel, and God loves us whether we can sense it all the time or not.

7. Why don't the things that God has already put in my spirit manifest automatically? Why do I have to do something to receive from God?

A. Everything that God has made available comes through the spirit. Whether or not it comes out of your spirit and into the physical realm where you can sense it, isn't dependent upon God; it's dependent upon whether or not *you believe* that God has already done it. The act of believing is the part we play in receiving the blessings that God has already provided.

This question will be answered much more in depth in the **Lesson** "Living in the Balance of Grace and Faith."

Additional Resources:

1. *You've Already Got It!* is a six-part audio teaching available to listen to or download for free at www.awmi.net/extra/audio/1033.

2. *You've Already Got It!*, the book by Andrew Wommack, teaches you how to experience the victory that is already yours. It is available through bookstores or the AWM online store at www.awmi.net/store/usa/books/320.

3. *How to Receive God's Best* is a five-part audio teaching. Blessings and miracles are both from God, but which method does He prefer in meeting your needs? When you understand this and put it into practice, you'll find peace, security, and stability in life. This teaching is available to listen to or download for free at www.awmi.net/extra/audio/1072.

4. *How to Be Happy* is a six-part audio teaching. Why are some people happy and others miserable? In this powerful series, you will learn the secrets of being happy. It is available to listen to or download for free at www.awmi.net/extra/audio/1019.

The True Nature of God
Lesson 5

> **Every good gift and every perfect gift is from above, and cometh down from the Father of lights, with whom is no variableness, neither shadow of turning.**
>
> JAMES 1:17

"In order to have a strong relationship with God, we need to know who He is. We need to understand His true nature, because it's impossible to be in a relationship with someone you don't know" (Sharper Than a Two-Edged Sword, Chapter 5).

NOTE TO LEADER: *The first question is to be asked to the student(s).*

1. **Can you recall a time in your life when someone got the wrong impression of you? How did it affect your relationship with that person?**

    A. In a similar way, many people have a wrong impression of God and His true nature because of events described in the Old Testament. The Old Testament contains examples of God smiting people with leprosy, sending a death angel into Egypt, flooding the earth, and destroying entire cities. I believe many people think that God is angry and wrathful because they have an incomplete perspective of those events. God *did* flood the earth and destroy cities, but those events have to be put into the proper frame of reference to understand His true nature.

2. **Is the God in the Old Testament different from the God of the New Testament? Did He change?**

    A. God was the same in the Old Testament as He is now. The Bible says, **"For I am the LORD, I change not"** (Mal. 3:6), and **"Jesus Christ the same yesterday, and to day, and for ever"** (Heb. 13:8). God is eternal and unchanging.

We, as human beings, have changed, and as a result, God has changed the way He deals with us. The change in how God deals with mankind is the difference we see when we read events in the Old Testament versus events in the New Testament.

B. Jesus is exactly like God the Father, and in His life, we see a perfect representation of who God is (Heb. 1:3). The love and compassion that caused Jesus to humble Himself and become a man and then to suffer death on a cross for us (John 3:16) is the exact same love that God had for humanity during the Old Testament. We need to read the Old Testament within that frame of reference and realize that God had to deal with people under the Old Covenant differently than He deals with us today.

But the Lord isn't dealing with us through the Law anymore. We have been saved by grace, and our born-again spirits allow God to deal with us in mercy. *Hallelujah!* We are finally capable of understanding spiritual things. We are able to know and understand the true nature of God: God is love, and His mercy toward us endures forever (Ps. 136).

3. What is the difference between the Old Covenant and the New Covenant?

A. The New Covenant is the covenant of salvation that Jesus made possible through His sacrifice. It refers to the fact that Jesus has restored us to a right relationship with God and that our born-again spirits have been made the righteousness of God in Christ Jesus (2 Cor. 5:21).

People alive in Old Testament times were spiritually dead and could not fully understand spiritual truth. Our ability to comprehend the things of God vastly increases with our new birth. Prior to being born again, we simply couldn't understand spiritual things. As the Apostle Paul explained it to the Corinthians, **"But the natural man receiveth not the things of the Spirit of God: for they are foolishness unto him: neither can he know them, because they are spiritually discerned"** (1 Cor. 2:14).

Under the Old Covenant, God needed to get people to resist evil and to resist the snares of the devil, but He couldn't do it by explanation, because they didn't have the capacity to understand spiritual reality. As a result, God was sometimes hard with people under the Old Covenant. Jesus came along and showed us the mercy and grace of God that the Old Testament didn't explain, but there is no conflict between the two. The nature of God has never changed.

4. Why did God give the Law to the Jews?

A. "The Law," in this sense, means "precepts" or "statutes" and is a reference to the Ten Commandments and the Pentateuch (the first five books of the Old Testament, written by Moses).

B. The Lord has always been merciful by nature. Until the Law was given—about 2,000 years *after* Adam and Eve sinned—God was relating to people by grace. God extended mercy to the first murderer on the face of the earth, Cain, but the first person to be stoned to death for breaking the Law was a man who was out gathering sticks on the Sabbath (Num. 15:32-36). The Law changed how God responded to sin, but the nature of God didn't change.

The Law was given for two main purposes: to show mankind God's high standard of perfection and to demonstrate that no one could achieve that standard through his or her own effort. The Law removed any illusion of self-righteousness and established man's need for a Savior. This is important because the Old Covenant and the New Covenant are not compatible. You can't be saved partially by your good works and then have Jesus make up where you fall short; it's all Jesus, or you aren't saved. The Apostle Paul wrote to the Galatians that if people were trying to save themselves, then Jesus couldn't help them (Gal. 5:2-4). The Law proves to us that our only hope is to be saved by grace through faith in Jesus (Eph. 2:8), and in the end, the Law served a merciful purpose

5. **Doesn't the Bible say somewhere that God uses hardship to teach us things and help us grow?**

   A. No. In fact, the Word of God says just the opposite: **"Let no man say when he is tempted, I am tempted of God: for God cannot be tempted with evil, neither tempteth he any man"** (James 1:13). And, **"Every good gift and every perfect gift is from above, and cometh down from the Father of lights, with whom is no variableness, neither shadow of turning"** (James 1:17).

   B. This topic is discussed more in depth during the **Lesson** "God Wants You Well."

   C. It's possible that someone will bring up the Old Testament book Job as an example that God uses tragedy to punish or test believers today. Here are eight reasons Job is no comparison for a New Covenant believer.

      i. Job is believed to be the oldest book in the Bible and was probably written even before Moses wrote the Pentateuch. Job lived after the Flood but probably before Abraham, and he had a limited revelation of the true nature of God (*Job was incapable of understanding God*, see point iii).

      ii. Job did not have understanding about Satan that we have available to us. He didn't know it is Satan who comes to steal, kill, and destroy (John 10:10). Not knowing who to blame, Job wrongly accused God.

      iii. Job had NO covenant with God. Job never mentions the Law, and he never appealed to having any covenant with God. (This is one explanation for why God withdrew His protection from Job: God didn't have a covenant with him and, therefore, had no "legal right" to protect him. Adam and Eve had turned dominion of the earth over to Satan, so when the devil challenged God on this point, He had to remove His hedge of protection that He had been providing out of grace.)

Job wasn't even protected by the Old Covenant. We have a better covenant established upon better promises (Heb. 8:6)—the New Covenant of deliverance through the blood of Jesus Christ. Our born-again spirits are new creations (2 Cor. 5:17), created in righteousness and true holiness (Eph. 4:24). We are the temple of God, and He would not defile His own temple (1 Cor. 3:16-17).

iv. Job didn't have any authority to rebuke the devil, but we do (Mark 16:17). Jesus has given us power of attorney to cast out demons in His name (Luke 10:19). We have been delivered from the powers of darkness (Col. 1:13). We aren't trying to get free from the powers of Satan—Jesus has already set us free!

v. Some mistakenly assume that Job was completely without sin in the entire account, but that isn't so.

   1. As Job's suffering wore on, he began to wrongly accuse God but repented when he was confronted by God (Job 42:1-6).

   2. Job's sin was that he was busy justifying himself, rather than God, throughout his ordeal (Job 32:2).

vi. Job's knowledge of God was from oral tradition and it was incomplete. We have maximum revelation of God because of Jesus. We know more truth than Job did.

The Apostle Peter wrote,

> **Grace and peace be multiplied unto you <u>through the knowledge of God</u>, and of Jesus our Lord, <u>According as his divine power hath</u> <u>given unto us all things that pertain unto life and godliness</u>, through the knowledge of him that hath called us to glory and virtue: Whereby are given unto us exceeding great and precious <u>promises: that by these ye</u> <u>might be partakers of the divine nature</u>, having escaped the corruption that is in the world through lust.**

2 PETER 1:2-4, UNDERLINES MINE

vii. Job lived in fear (Job 3:25-26) because he had no covenant with God and, therefore, no confidence. But believers have been delivered from fear. The Word says, **"For God hath not given us the spirit of fear; but of power, and of love, and of a sound mind"** (2 Tim. 1:7).

And speaking of Jesus, it says, **"Forasmuch then as the children are partakers of flesh and blood, he also himself likewise took part of the same; that through death he might destroy him that had the power of death, that is, the devil; And deliver them who through fear of death were all their lifetime subject to bondage"** (Heb. 2:14-15). We don't have to live in fear the way Job did.

viii. Job had no intercessor, but *we have Jesus, who is able to save us and who lives to make intercession for us* (Heb. 7:25)! And if Jesus is for us, then who can be against us? Because of our New Covenant, nothing can separate us from the love of God (Rom. 8:31 and 38-39), and God will never leave us nor forsake us (Heb. 13:5).

6. If God is good and all powerful, then why is there so much tragedy and suffering in the world?

A. Tragedy is a result of sin. When sin entered the world, man became spiritually separated from God, the planet was corrupted and transformed from a state of perfection to instability, and man gave dominion of the world over to Satan.

Most of the tragedy we see in the world is the result of the spiritual separation of mankind from God because of sin. Our own sin can cause tragedy in our lives (e.g., wrong choices that bring suffering), and other people's sin can cause tragedy in our lives (e.g., crimes, abuse, and other wrong choices carried out against us).

A major reason God doesn't stop all evil from happening in the world is that He doesn't want to violate mankind's free will. Free will is the only means we have of receiving salvation and eternal life from God. If God were to intervene and stop someone from making wrong choices, He would be taking away free will and removing mankind's only hope of redemption through Jesus. Still, the Bible is full of stories showing God stepping in to protect His people, and we won't know how much evil God has prevented in our lives until we get to heaven.

We also see loss of life and tragedy as a result of natural disasters. This is a result of the planet taking on sin and becoming unstable. Romans says, **"For we know that the whole creation groaneth and travaileth in pain together until now"** (Rom. 8:22). Creation itself was negatively affected by sin, and it won't be completely healed until Jesus comes again and creates a new heaven and a new earth (Rev. 21:1).

God is not responsible for the tragedy in our world. In fact, Jesus came so that He might destroy the works of the devil (1 John 3:8) and set us free from the bondage of death (Heb. 2:14). Mankind bears some responsibility for tragedy when it results from the choices of an individual. The fallen nature of the world we live in also causes tragedy. And, finally, we have an Enemy who roams about seeking to destroy people's lives (John 10:10 and 1 Pet. 5:8).

But God has more than compensated for our suffering. Jesus knows our suffering (Heb. 4:15) and warned that we will have troubles in this world, but He said, **"Be of good cheer; I have overcome the world"** (John 16:33). God is able to heal us of the pain that results from tragedy, and He can give us the strength to endure. Although God doesn't cause tragedy and we should always resist problems (James 4:7), God can still make all things work out for our benefit (Rom. 8:28).

Additionally, the Holy Spirit comforts us, His joy and peace reside in our spirits, and we have the promise that one day, there will be no more suffering. Of the day when Jesus comes again, it is written, **"And God shall wipe away all tears from their eyes; and there shall be no more death, neither sorrow, nor crying, neither shall there be any more pain: for the former things are passed away"** (Rev. 21:4).

7. **Does God send disaster (terrorist attacks, war, hurricanes, natural disasters, etc.) as a judgment for sin?**

   A. God sent Jesus to reconcile the world to Himself while we were still in sin. The Bible says, **"But God commendeth his love toward us, in that, while we were yet sinners, Christ died for us"** (Rom. 5:8), and **"To wit, that God was in Christ, reconciling the world unto himself, not imputing their trespasses unto them; and hath committed unto us the word of reconciliation"** (2 Cor. 5:19). The Word of God also states that God doesn't want anyone to perish but for all to come to repentance, or be saved (1 Tim. 2:4 and 2 Pet. 3:9). Sending disaster in any form as judgment for sin would be in contradiction to God's Word, and we know that God does not go back on His Word (Num. 23:19 and Ps. 89:34).

   God is not judging the world at this time: **"For God sent not his Son into the world to condemn the world; but that the world through him might be saved"** (John 3:17). There will come a time when there is judgment for sin, but the only sin that is going to be judged is the one sin that wasn't paid for on the cross—the sin of failing to believe in Jesus' redemptive work (this is also the only sin that the Holy Spirit is convicting people of, John 16:7-9).

   God doesn't send disaster and tragedy as judgment for sin (see also note 5 and 6). Jesus touched on this during His ministry (Luke 13:1-5) when He explained that a person suffering a tragedy doesn't mean the person is a worse sinner than those who escape it; it just means the earth is a fallen world. But if we fail to choose Jesus now, we will die in the sense of failing to be united with God in eternity—and that is the ultimate tragedy.

Additional Resources:

1. *The True Nature of God* is a five-part audio teaching available to listen to or download for free at www.awmi.net/extra/audio/1002.

2. *The True Nature of God*, the book by Andrew Wommack, traces God's dealings with man all the way from the Garden of Eden to the present and shows one consistent nature of God through it all. This teaching will answer many questions and leave you with a much greater faith in the goodness of God. It is available through bookstores or the AWM online store at www.awmi.net/store/usa/books/308.

3. *The Good Report: Why Bad Things Happen* is a compilation of articles in booklet form on the topic of why bad things happen. It is available through the AWM online store at www.awmi.net/store/usa/books/101.

4. "The Sovereignty of God" is an audio teaching available to listen to or download for free at www.awmi.net/extra/audio/authority.

The War Is Over
Lesson 6

And suddenly there was with the angel a multitude of the heavenly host praising God, and saying, Glory to God in the highest, and on earth peace, good will toward men.

LUKE 2:13-14

"Jesus suffered the wrath and rejection of God so that we might be made the righteousness of God in Him. As a result, God isn't mad anymore. Jesus bore our punishment, and the war is over" (Sharper Than a Two-Edged Sword, Chapter 6*).*

1. **So, God isn't mad at me when I do something wrong? How can that be?**

    A.   When man sinned, God declared war on sin. He set Himself against evil, and man got caught in the middle of the war. Sometimes in war, collateral damage is inflicted while trying to defeat the enemy. Because of the sin nature and the decisions made by man, people were tangled up with evil and were targeted by God's fight against sin. God was right to be upset and angry over the sin of people in the Old Testament, and His punishments were just. But things have changed. God isn't at war with sin anymore. Jesus won the fight.

    God's wrath and punishment against sin in the Old Testament isn't seen in the New Testament. For instance, Elijah called down fire from heaven and killed 102 men, but when Jesus' disciples wanted to do the same thing, He rebuked them, saying, **"Ye know not what manner of spirit ye are of. For the Son of man is not come to destroy men's lives, but to save them"** (Luke 9:55-56). In the New Covenant, after Jesus came, the war ended. Jesus forever satisfied God's demand for justice and payment for sin. Jesus bore our sin and suffered for us. He took all of God's anger against sin upon Himself, and now the wrath of God has been totally satisfied.

2. **How could the suffering of one man pay the price for all sin, for all time?**

    A.   When Jesus was lifted up on the cross, He drew all judgment for sin upon Himself. All of God's wrath—not just a portion of it—came upon Jesus. Jesus was like a lightning rod: When He was lifted up on the cross, all of the anger and punishment of God toward the sin of man came upon the physical body of Jesus. God satisfied every demand of justice by punishing His own Son for our sins, and not only for the sin committed up until that time but also for all sin for all time (Heb. 10:10). Every single sin—past, present, and future—was satisfied. Jesus suffered the wrath and rejection of God so that we might be made the righteousness of God in Him. As a result, God isn't mad anymore. Jesus bore our punishment, and the war is over.

Jesus abolished the Law upon the cross and brought peace between God and man (Eph. 2:15). Some people have a hard time believing that such a tremendous statement could be true. They can't believe that one person's suffering could atone for all of the billions and billions of people who have ever lived—or will ever live—on the face of the earth. The difficulty in comprehending this arises because we don't understand the value God placed upon the obedience of His Son to suffer and die for us. Jesus wasn't only a man; He was God in the flesh of a man. His life as God was worth more than the entire human race put together.

3. **I know God paid for all sin, but I still have to go to confession or do penance every time I sin in order to *stay* in right standing with God, don't I?**

A. Jesus was God manifest in the flesh. Through His suffering and death, He paid more than twice what the entire human race owed for sin (Is. 40:1-2). Some churches are preaching that every time you sin, it's a new infraction against God, and He won't answer your prayers or fellowship with you until you get right with Him again. They are saying that the war isn't over. They think there is just a temporary lull in the hostilities. The moment you sin, they say, God's wrath is rekindled against you. Essentially, they are saying that Jesus' sacrifice wasn't enough to atone for sin. They are teaching that atonement is in Jesus' suffering *plus* your suffering, but that isn't true. Jesus' suffering alone more than paid the price.

God isn't mad at you, even when you sin, because His war against sin is over. There is peace from God toward you (Rom. 5:1), and it all centers on Jesus: If you accept Jesus, who paid for your sins, then God is not angry at you.

When you discover that you have sinned, you should *repent*—change the direction you are going and/or the way you are thinking—but God doesn't require penance. Penance is the religious ritual of expressing sorrow, confessing your sin to a clergy member, and accepting punishment for your sin, in order to be "absolved," washed clean, or pardoned of sin. Jesus has already absolved us of sin, and it's only our relationship with Him that makes us clean. Repentance is necessary because it gets us back on track to walking with God, but after you are born again, sin is no longer an issue with God. Sin affects us, but it doesn't change the way God relates to us.

4. **Since God isn't holding sin against me, why do I have to turn over my whole life to Him? Can't I just keep sinning in one small area of my life—especially if it has become a hard habit to break? What harm will it do?**

   A. God isn't holding sin against you anymore, but that doesn't mean you can go live in sin. God still loves you if you are living in sin, but sin is stupid because it opens up a door to the devil. The devil only comes to steal, kill, and destroy (John 10:10), so you don't want to open yourself up to his attacks. You're dumb if you live that way, but God still loves you.

   Sinning, even in a small thing, isn't smart, because it hardens your heart toward God (Heb. 3:13), and it's a form of neglecting the Lord, which is the first step in desensitizing yourself to Him. (I talk more about the importance of this in the **Lessons** "Hardness of Heart" and "Staying Full of God.")

5. **If the war is over, then why is there going to be a judgment when Jesus comes?**

   A. When Jesus was lifted up on the cross, He drew all judgment for sin unto Himself, and now the war is over. God is at peace toward you. Jesus saved us from the wrath of God.

   Still, even though salvation is available to everyone, it isn't automatic. We still have to make the choice to receive the salvation that Jesus has made available. Fortunately, God has made receiving salvation so simple that all we have to do is believe in the redemptive work of Jesus and submit to His Lordship.

   However, all who refuse to receive salvation are refusing relationship with God, and relationship with God is the only path to avoid judgment for sin. God's will is for everyone to be saved (1 Tim. 2:4), but He won't make that choice for them. The judgment that will occur when Jesus comes again isn't a reflection of God's love for humanity or His judgment upon sin; it's just the separation of those who have received God's gift of salvation, from those who have refused it.

Additional Resources:

1. *The War Is Over* is a five-part audio teaching available to listen to or download for free at www.awmi.net/extra/audio/1053.

2. *The War Is Over*, a book by Andrew Wommack, shows how the longest conflict in history lasted 4,000 years and ended in a decisive victory nearly 2,000 years ago—in Jesus' death and resurrection. The answers in this book will release you from the condemnation of judgment and fear. It will free you to receive the promised blessings of God! It is available through bookstores or the AWM online store at www.awmi.net/store/usa/books/326.

3. *How to Deal with Temptation* is a five-part audio teaching that shows us the right way and the wrong way to respond when tempted, and the way to avoid being tempted altogether. It is available to listen to or download for free at www.awmi.net/extra/audio/1049.

Grace, the Power of the Gospel
Lesson 7

> **For I am not ashamed of the gospel of Christ: for it is the power of God unto salvation to every one that believeth.**
>
> **ROMANS 1:16**

"Jesus briefly became what we were—separated from God—so that we could become what He is: a son of God, accepted and in right relationship with Him. Jesus took all of our sin and gave us all of His righteousness" (Sharper Than a Two-Edged Sword, Chapter 7).

1. **What is the difference between a works-based approach to salvation and a grace-based approach?**

    A. A works-based approach to salvation is trying to earn relationship with God by being good—it's like saying you deserve salvation because of the way you have lived. A lot of people today don't understand that being good or living holy won't save you. They think that if they're good people, they're going to be okay. But being good isn't *good enough*. God's standard of holiness is impossible for man to achieve.

    We may look good compared to other people, but there is no comparison to the holiness of God. Jesus was the express image of God's glory and of His purpose (Heb. 1:3). Jesus is God's standard for holiness: never committing a single sin, of commission or omission, in thought or deed, from birth until death. There is no such thing as "almost perfect." Either you're perfect or you aren't, and we aren't—that's why we need a Savior.

    A grace-based approach recognizes that our own efforts can never save us but simply believing in Jesus will. The Gospel, or good news, is that the burden of salvation is not on our shoulders, and we don't have to do anything to earn it. Salvation, healing, and deliverance don't depend on our goodness. Jesus has already earned everything for us, and all we have to do is believe!

2. **Do you think that lost people need to be reminded of why they aren't in right relationship with God? Why or why not?**

    A. Paul wasn't ashamed to tell people the good news. He wasn't ashamed *not* to beat people over the head with their sinfulness and inadequacy. The vast majority of people don't need to have their sin amplified before them. What they need is to hear the *nearly-too-good-to-be-true news* that Jesus died to make them righteous, and all they need to do is believe.

        The man who helped get me really excited about the Lord when I was a teenager had been raised in a religious environment. He knew that God was real, but before he was saved, he lived a sinful lifestyle. His problems with alcohol and sexual immorality were well-known in the community. A man from my church used to go to his house every Saturday to tell him what a sinner he was and how he'd better repent. But my friend already knew he was a sinner. He didn't need to hear more information about how sorry and ungodly he was. He was saved when he learned about the grace of God through the Gospel of Jesus Christ.

        A lot of people today are in the same situation that my friend was in. They are being turned off and driven away from God by religion. Religion is pounding them with how sinful and sorry they are, but they already know that at the heart level, even if they won't admit it. What they need is to hear the Gospel, the good news that Jesus died to take their sin and return them to right relationship with the Father.

3. **How is my performance as a Christian connected to God answering my prayers and using His power to help me in life?**

    A. God is no longer relating to you based on your performance. He is relating to you based on the righteousness of your spirit. Jesus earned righteousness for all of mankind on the cross, and you became a new creation when you believed (2 Cor. 5:17-21). All of this came by the grace of God. Ephesians says, **"For by grace are ye saved through faith; and that not of yourselves: it is the gift of God: Not of works, lest any man should boast"** (Eph. 2:8-9).

        God answers your prayers regardless of your performance, and His power is always available to help you. However, sin does affect you. It doesn't change how God relates to you, but it changes how you relate to God. Faith is the conduit through which God's power flows, and sin will harden your heart and make it harder for you to have faith to receive from God.

NOTE TO LEADER: The following questions are to be asked to the student(s).

4. **What do you think the Gospel message is? (Take a moment to briefly summarize the essence of the Gospel, and then discuss.)**

    A. Explanations will vary, but they should share some common elements. For example: Jesus is God, yet because of His great love for us, He left His glory with the Father, humbled Himself, and became a man. He became a man to destroy the works of the devil and restore mankind to relationship with God.

    Because of the sin nature in mankind, we have all sinned and fallen short of the glory of God. It isn't the sins we committed that caused us to be sinners; it's the sin nature in us that caused us to sin—and the wages of sin is death. Even if we could've have quit sinning, it would've done nothing to erase what we had done in the past. There was nothing we could do to save ourselves.

    In the midst of our hopeless situation, God sent His Son to live a holy life and to earn everything we could not do on our own. Jesus deserved the blessing of God, but instead, He took all of our sins upon Himself, and through His death and resurrection, He gave us His holiness and goodness in exchange.

    Jesus bore our sin and paid the debt we couldn't pay. Jesus briefly became what we were—separated from God—so that we could become what He is: a son of God, accepted and in right relationship with Him. Jesus took all of our sin and gave us all of His righteousness. Jesus delivered us from sin and its effects. He took our sickness on the cross so that we could be free from the curse of sin and sickness in this life.

    We are now accepted with God, and our acceptance isn't based on how holy we are; it's based on the sacrifice Jesus made for us. Jesus has paid the price for salvation. All we have to do is recognize our need for it and accept the free gift of relationship with God through Jesus Christ. We accept the gift of salvation by confessing that Jesus is Lord and believing in our hearts that God raised Him from the dead (Rom. 10:9-10).

5. **Does your summary of the Gospel stir up a sense of gratitude for what God has done in your life? Does your summary sound to you like nearly-too-good-to-be-true news?**

    A. Discuss what you might add to, or take away from, your summary to make it the nearly-too-good-to-be-true news of Jesus Christ.

Additional Resources:

1. *The Gospel: The Power of God* is a four-part audio teaching discussing grace and the book of Romans. It is available to listen to or download for free at www.awmi. net/extra/audio/1014.

2. *Grace, the Power of the Gospel*, a book by Andrew Wommack, shows that it isn't what you do but what Christ did that makes you righteous. Never again worry if you are meeting God's holy standard. This book is available through bookstores or the AWM online store at www.awmi.net/store/usa/books/322.

3. "The Grace of Giving" is an audio teaching that shows how grace relates to giving. It is available to listen to or download for free at www.awmi.net/extra/audio/finance.

4. "Grace and Faith in Giving" is an audio teaching that shows us how to trust God with our finances. It is available to listen to or download for free at www.awmi. net/extra/audio/finance.

5. *God's Kind of Love: The Cure for What Ails Ya!* is a three-part audio teaching that talks about how much God loves us. You can't give what you haven't received. Before you can love others, you have to have a true revelation of God's love for you. This series will help you receive a deeper revelation of God's unconditional love for you. It is available to listen to or download for free at www.awmi.net/extra/audio/1015.

Living in the Balance of Grace and Faith
Lesson 8

For by grace are ye saved through faith; and that not of yourselves: it is the gift of God: Not of works, lest any man should boast.

EPHESIANS 2:8-9

"God has already provided everything we will ever need— that's grace—but we have to reach out and take it by faith" (Sharper Than a Two-Edged Sword, Chapter 8).

1. What is grace?

A. Grace is what God does for you independently of what you deserve. God's grace has nothing to do with you. The Greek word that we translate "grace" in the Bible literally means unearned, undeserved favor—but it's even more than that. Grace is something God did for you prior to you having a need for it. God extended His grace to you before you even existed.

God's grace came to earth through Jesus 2,000 years ago. When Jesus died on the cross, He died for all sin, for all time: past, present, and future. Jesus paid for our sin 2,000 years before we were born. God didn't look down and say, "They're such wonderful people, and they are trying so hard. I think I'll do something to help them." No, God anticipated our human state and our sin, and He paid the price before we were alive. Before the problem had come into existence, God had created the solution. That is grace.

If you had to be worthy in order to get God's grace, it wouldn't be grace; it would be a payment you earn in exchange for your own goodness. God's grace is given independently of you. Grace is all God.

2. What is faith?

A. Before defining what faith is, I want to talk about what faith is not. Faith is not something you do to get God to respond to you or to act on your behalf. Anything you will ever need has already been provided by grace, including salvation, healing, deliverance, joy, peace, and prosperity. It's true that faith will cause the power of God to come into manifestation, but it isn't because God is responding to your faith. Faith doesn't move God. It moves you into position to receive what God has already provided by grace.

Faith is simply our positive response to God's grace.

It took me twenty years to understand those few words. Faith doesn't *cause* a positive response from God; He has already provided all things by grace. ***Faith is just your positive response to what God has already provided.*** Another way of saying it is that faith only appropriates what God has already provided by grace. If God hasn't already provided it independently of your efforts and prior to your need, then your faith can't make it happen.

3. What effect can being out of balance in the area of grace have upon my life?

   A. Grace out of balance means you believe that everything is determined by God's grace. You can take the truth that God moves in our lives independently of our performance too far. By overemphasizing God's grace, you can erroneously conclude that *everything* is up to God and that *nothing* happens unless it is His will. This doctrine is often called "the sovereignty of God." It is deadly for two reasons.

      First, it renders believers passive. They conclude that everything happens purely by God's will and that they have no part to play. But if this is true, why bother making any effort in life? Eventually, they think there is no point in seeking God, reading the Word, or pursuing relationship with the Lord.

      Second, this extreme doctrine erodes trust. If nothing can happen but what God wills, then God would be responsible for all of the evil in life and in the world—which is absolutely not true (James 1:17). God isn't causing the tragedy in your life, but if you *think* He is, you won't trust Him.

      The Word says to submit to God and resist the devil, but if you think God is causing tragedy, you won't know what to resist and what to submit to (James 4:7). Satan will not flee unless you resist him, and the extreme-sovereignty false doctrine has some people confused and submitting to the devil (by believing that the sickness and tragedy in their lives are God's will). Satan only comes to steal, kill, and destroy (John 10:10), and if you submit to him, that is exactly what he will try to do.

      This extreme sovereignty teaching is the basis of Calvinism.

   B. Review "The True Nature of God" **Lesson** for a more detailed discussion of why God is not the source of tragedy in the world.

4. What effect will taking an extreme view of faith have upon my relationship with God?

A. The extreme view of faith leads people to believe that their faith controls every outcome. But faith doesn't move God. Faith isn't something people do to make God respond to their situation or request. Their faith isn't going to *make* God do anything.

Some people have this concept that they are going to grab hold of God and not let go until He gives them what they want. They think, *I'm going to make God heal this person, I'm going to make God prosper me,* or *I'm going to make my spouse stay with me.* But faith doesn't make God do anything. If it wasn't provided in the atonement of Jesus, their faith can't make it happen. All faith does is reach out and partake of what God has already provided by grace.

5. If I have the faith, will God give me absolutely anything I desire? Why or why not?

A. The Gospel of Mark says,

> **For verily I say unto you, That whosoever shall say unto this mountain, Be thou removed, and be thou cast into the sea; and shall not doubt in his heart, but shall believe that those things which he saith shall come to pass; he shall have whatsoever he saith. Therefore I say unto you, What things soever ye desire, when ye pray, believe that ye receive them, and ye shall have them.**
>
> **MARK 11:23-24**

These verses say that whatever things you desire, when you pray, believe that you receive them, and you will have them. People who take an extreme view of faith have misinterpreted this to indicate that they can have whatever they want, provided they have the faith to believe for it. This misunderstanding of faith has led some to have false expectations of what is possible by faith, sometimes with bizarre results.

I remember a woman in Arlington, Texas, who was in the extreme-faith camp and was teaching it to her students at a Bible school she opened. She took this scripture that says you can have **"what things soever ye desire"** and decided she wanted Kenneth Copeland (a well-known minister) as her husband. The problem was that he was already married to Gloria. So, this woman held a mock wedding where she married Kenneth "in the spirit," and then she "stood in faith" waiting for Gloria to die and get out of her way so she could unite with Kenneth.

Most people would recognize there was something wrong with that picture. **"What things soever ye desire"** isn't a free ticket to receive by faith anything that strikes your fancy. *Faith only appropriates what God has already provided by grace.* God didn't provide murder and adultery through the atonement of Jesus, so you can't believe for someone to die in order to take his or her spouse.

6. **Can you give me an example from the Bible that shows how God's will doesn't automatically come to pass?**

    A. God doesn't control all things: who gets saved, who gets healed, who marries whom, and on down to the finest details of life.

        The Bible says, **"For the grace of God that bringeth salvation hath appeared to all men"** (Titus 2:11).

        If salvation was purely up to God and if grace alone saved, then all would be saved because God's grace has appeared to all. God's grace was extended prior to your existence, and it has nothing to do with you. So, if grace by itself was sufficient for salvation, you would already be saved when you are born. No further action on your part would be required. But you aren't saved by grace alone; you're saved by grace *through* faith (Eph. 2:8).

        It isn't up to God whether or not you get saved. The Scripture says, **"The Lord is not slack concerning his promise, as some men count slackness; but is longsuffering to us-ward, not willing that any should perish, but that all should come to repentance"** (2 Pet. 3:9).

        God desires that everyone be saved, but not everyone will be, because it isn't God's decision. Salvation comes by the grace of God, but people have to respond with faith. Grace is God's part; faith is man's. It is faith in God's grace that releases the power of salvation in people. Everything is available by the grace of God, but there has to be a faith response on their part to receive what is available by grace.

    B. A few Christian denominations have misunderstood God's grace and teach that He has chosen and predestined certain people for heaven or hell—because they believe everything is completely and totally determined by Him. This erroneous doctrine is called "unconditional election." It is the view that God selected some people for salvation before creation, and those people are chosen apart from meeting any conditions.

        "Unconditional election" is proven false by the Scriptures, which show that it is God's will for all to be saved but not all will be. It is another example of overemphasizing the grace of God.

C. God is sovereign in the sense that He ranks first and has supreme power and rank. I agree with that 100 percent. Nobody tells God what to do. He is absolutely supreme.

I don't disagree with the truth that God is sovereign. I disagree with the misuse of the word "sovereign" by those who have twisted the grace of God and fallen into error.

7. What is the balance of grace and faith?

A. When God created Adam and Eve, He created everything they would ever need. Not only did God anticipate their needs, but He also anticipated the needs of all the people who would ever live on the face of the earth. God created this world with enough oxygen to sustain Adam and Eve and as many descendants as would ever exist on this planet. He created enough food to feed all of earth's inhabitants. There's a reason Adam and Eve weren't created until the sixth day: If He had created them first, they would have had to tread water for two days until there was land to stand on. Then they would have had to dodge the mountains and trees as they sprung up from the earth. God anticipated everything.

God created all things, and by grace, He provided for all of the needs that Adam and Eve would ever have. Still, their needs weren't automatically fulfilled. Adam and Eve had a part to play. They had to reach out and partake of God's grace. God provided fruit to eat, for instance, but they had to take it and eat. The Lord didn't create them with tubes into their stomachs so they could be fed without any effort on their part. They had to gather and use what God had provided. If they had sat around waiting for God to spoon-feed them every meal, they would have starved to death.

In the same way, God has already provided everything we will ever need— that's grace—but we have to reach out and take it by faith.

You don't make God heal you; God has already provided for your healing through grace. What you do is reach out and take that healing by faith. Your faith doesn't make healing happen any more than Adam and Eve, by reaching out their arms, made a tree shoot from the ground and sprout fruit. The trees were already there, but Adam and Eve had to harvest the fruit. Likewise, you have a part to play in reaching out to obtain God's promises. Your part is faith.

Believers in the extreme-grace camp are saying that everything comes by the grace of God and that they don't see any role for themselves. Their approach to life is *que sera, sera*—"whatever will be, will be." People with this attitude don't see the point in doing anything or even seeking God, because they believe everything has already been determined by His grace. They end up floating lazily down the river of life, waiting to see what happens next.

Believers in the extreme-faith camp recognize that they have a role to play, but they overemphasize that role. They understand that God's will doesn't automatically come to pass, and they focus on how important it is for them to do things (read the Word, pray, have faith, etc.). If people aren't careful, they can fall into believing that it is their own actions that are producing results. They can start to think that their goodness is making God move on their behalf, which leads to pride and Phariseeism.

Anytime a truth from God's Word is taken to an extreme or to the exclusion of other truths, it leads to error. Faith is poison by itself, and grace is poison by itself. *But when you put faith in what God has already done by grace, it becomes a combination you can't live without. It's the balance of grace and faith, and it will release the power of God in your life.*

Additional Resources:

1. *Living in the Balance of Grace and Faith* is a five-part audio teaching available to listen to or download for free at www.awmi.net/extra/audio/1064.

2. *Living in the Balance of Grace and Faith*, a book by Andrew Wommack, gives a correct understanding of grace and faith and how they work together. In this book, Andrew clearly explains both concepts and how living in the balance of the two will change your relationship with God forever. It is available through bookstores or the AWM online store at www.awmi.net/store/usa/books/228.

3. *Insights into Faith* is a booklet by Andrew Wommack that consists of a compilation of footnotes from the *Life for Today Study Bible* on the subject of faith. These notes have been organized and tied together to produce a short yet powerful book that will build your faith. It is available through the online store at www.awmi.net/store/usa/books/100.

4. "The Faith of God" is an audio teaching that discusses the difference between human faith and spiritual faith. It is available to listen to or download for free at www.awmi.net/extra/audio/faith.

The Believer's Authority
Lesson 9

And as ye go, preach, saying, The kingdom of heaven is at hand. Heal the sick, cleanse the lepers, raise the dead, cast out devils: freely ye have received, freely give.

MATTHEW 10:7-8

"I believe that the number-one reason for unanswered prayer is that people are asking God to do something He has given us the power and authority to do for ourselves" (Sharper Than a Two-Edged Sword, Chapter 9).

1. **What's the big difference between asking God to heal and me commanding sickness to leave?**

   A. The same power that raised Christ from the dead is now dwelling in you (Eph. 1:19-20). Whenever you approach God as if you are powerless to change your situation, you reveal that you don't understand the power He has given you. You might be asking for the right thing or seeking the right results, but you're going about it in the wrong way. Miracles don't come to pass that way. The Scripture says, **"Submit yourselves therefore to God. Resist the devil, and he will flee from you"** (James 4:7).

   God told you to resist the devil, and the devil will flee. The word **"resist"** means to actively fight against. It is your responsibility to resist the devil. You can't go to God and ask Him to get the devil off your back; you have to fight against the devil yourself.

   Sickness and disease are works of the devil (John 10:10), so when you ask God to heal your sickness, you are, in effect, asking Him to rebuke the devil for you. But God told *you* to resist the devil. If you don't resist the devil, he won't go away. You can beg and plead with God until you're blue in the face—you can give Him all the ins and outs of how desperate your situation is—but nothing is going to happen until you resist the devil yourself.

2. **Since I have the authority to use God's power, do I still need God in order to heal the sick?**

   A. On our own, we can't heal a fly—but we're never on our own. The Lord has promised that He will never leave us nor forsake us (Heb. 13:5). After we are born again, God places His power on the inside of us—power over all sickness and disease and over every demon. God has given us His power and authority to heal the sick, but it's still His power. We don't have to ask Him to heal the sick or cast demons out for us, but we also can't do it without Him.

It's God's power, but it's our responsibility to put it to use.

3. **Why won't God just heal me right now and get it over with? Why do I have to cooperate with Him?**

    A.   Speaking of Jesus, the Bible says, **"Who being the brightness of his glory, and the express image of his person, and upholding all things by the word of his power, when he had by himself purged our sins, sat down on the right hand of the Majesty on high"** (Heb. 1:3).

            Jesus was a perfect, identical representation of the Father, and He upholds all things by the Word of His power. This universe is held together by the power of Jesus' words. If Jesus ever violated the integrity of His Word, then things would cease to be held together, and the universe would be destroyed. It isn't an option for God to tell us to do something and then to go back on His word and do it for us. God doesn't go back on His Word (Ps. 89:34).

            God wants us well, but He will not violate His Word to heal us. God told us to resist the devil, and if we don't do it—for whatever reason—He isn't going to do it for us. He gave us raising-from-the-dead power, but we have to believe and resist the devil. It is absolutely God's will for us to be healed of sickness, but we have to learn to cooperate with Him to receive healing. This subject is discussed further during the **Lessons** "Living in the Balance of Grace and Faith" and "God Wants You Well."

4. **Satan has no power over God, and God lives in me. So, Satan can't have any impact on my life, right?**

    A.   God lives in all born-again believers, and He has delivered you from the powers of darkness (Col. 1:13), so Satan can't control you outside of your will. He can't have any impact on your life unless you allow him to. *But*, if you yield yourself to the devil (Rom. 6:16), he will come into your life to steal, kill, and destroy (John 10:10). Embracing attacks from the Enemy upon your finances, family, or health, as well as habitually committing sin, are a couple of ways you can yield yourself to the devil.

            God gave us the command, **"Submit yourselves therefore to God. Resist the devil, and he will flee from you"** (James 4:7). As long as you submit to God *and* resist the devil, the Enemy has no inroad into your life.

5. If I don't see any results immediately after I pray, did anything happen?

A. Fig trees are unique fruit trees because they produce fruit at the same time that they leaf out. So, when the tree is full of green leaves, it should have fruit as well. Scripture records that one day, Jesus saw a fig tree with leaves from a distance and walked to it, wanting to find food. When He got to the tree, it didn't have any fruit. It looked like it had fruit on it, but it didn't. It was symbolic of religious hypocrisy. The tree was professing to possess something that it didn't really have. Seeing this, Jesus cursed the fig tree. The next day, they walked by the tree, and it was dead. It had dried up from the roots (Mark 11:20).

The moment Jesus spoke to the tree, it died, but it took twenty-four hours for what had happened to become visible. This is important to remember when you pray. The effects of prayer are not always immediately evident to your senses, but power always goes forth when you pray in the name of Jesus. If you wait patiently in faith, expecting to see what you pray for, then you will see it come to pass. As the disciples passed by the dried-up fig tree, Peter pointed out to Jesus that it had died:

> **And Jesus answering saith unto them, Have faith in God. For verily I say unto you, That whosoever shall say unto this mountain, Be thou removed, and be thou cast into the sea; and shall not doubt in his heart, but shall believe that those things which he saith shall come to pass; he shall have whatsoever he saith. Therefore I say unto you, What things soever ye desire, when ye pray, believe that ye receive them, and ye shall have them.**
>
> **MARK 11:22-24**

It took a day for the tree to dry up from the roots and die, but the moment Jesus spoke, power went forth and began accomplishing His will. The Bible says, **"So shall my word be that goeth forth out of my mouth: it shall not return unto me void, but it shall accomplish that which I please, and it shall prosper in the thing whereto I sent it"** (Is. 55:11). God's Word always works, and it will work for you if you believe when you pray.

It might take time for the evidence to appear in the physical realm where your senses can perceive it, but the moment you speak to your problem in the name of Jesus, power goes forth to accomplish His purpose.

6. How is it that words have power?

A. Jesus stressed the power of words when He explained to the disciples what had happened to the fig tree (Mark 11:22-24). Three times in that passage, the Lord emphasized the power of words. Jesus didn't touch the fig tree or try to pull it down; He just spoke to it. Everything in creation was made by the power of God's Word (Gen. 1 and Heb. 11:3).

All that is necessary to release the faith and power that God has given you is to speak to your problem. Faith and power are released through words. Jesus said **"Whosoever shall *say*"** (Mark 11:23, emphasis mine) and believe the things he or she *says* will have whatsoever he or she *says*. Words are powerful.

Proverbs says, **"Death and life are in the power of the tongue: and they that love it shall eat the fruit thereof"** (Prov. 18:21). The miracle you are waiting for is in your mouth—if you would speak and not doubt. The problem is when you say things you don't believe with your whole heart. You waver and the Bible says that those who waver don't receive anything from God (James 1:6-8). Jesus said that when you pray, you have to believe and not doubt in your heart. You can't waver. You have to speak and believe.

7. How do I need to pray against something to effectively use the power God has given me?

A. When you have an obstacle, or problem, in your way, you need to *speak directly to the problem*. Most Christians spend ten minutes describing the problem, and the next ten seconds begging God to make it go away. "O God," they cry, "please move this mountain." But that is a totally wrong approach. God didn't tell you to talk to Him about your problem and ask Him to make them go away. He told you to speak to the mountain and cast it into the sea (Mark 11:23).

I once prayed for a woman who had severe pain throughout her body. The pain had been present for seven years, and the date that doctors predicted she would die had passed three years before I even met her. She was in terrible shape. I explained to her the source of the believer's authority and the need to speak directly to the problem, and then I prayed with her. She was instantly healed and started praising God.

After she was healed, I spent another twenty minutes teaching her not to quit believing that God healed her. Feeling a symptom of illness after you have prayed doesn't mean you weren't healed. It's like the fig tree that dried up from the roots: Sometimes it takes a little time to see the healing fully manifest to your senses.

Also, the devil is going to probe to see if you really believed when you prayed. He'll come with symptoms, like a knock at your door, to see if you'll open up and let him back in. The devil wants to see if he can get you to back off of believing that God healed you. One of the ways he does it is by bringing back symptoms or thoughts that remind you of being sick. If you ever have another pain or symptom, just speak to it. Believe that God has given you power; then resist the pain or sickness, and it will flee from you.

When the woman and I were done talking, she started to leave, but as soon as she touched the doorknob to open the door, she told me the stinging pain returned. I reminded her that I had just spent twenty minutes teaching her what to do, and I told her that I would agree with her as she prayed.

She said, "I claim my healing, in the name of Jesus. By Your stripes, I was healed." She prayed for a little while longer and said some good things, but she didn't take her authority and speak directly to the problem.

"Do you still have any stinging?" I asked her.

"Yes," she said.

"Do you know why?" I asked.

"No," she replied.

"It's because you didn't talk to the stinging," I told her. "You talked to God and confessed your faith in God, but you didn't take your authority and speak to the problem."

"You mean I'm supposed to say, 'Stinging be gone, in the name of Jesus?'"

"Exactly," I said.

We joined hands to pray again and she said, "Stinging, in Jesus' name…"

That's as far as she got before the stinging fled her body. It's been eight years or so, and she has been totally free of that problem ever since.

God has placed His power and authority on the inside of you, but it is your responsibility to use it. Once you begin to use what God has given you, instead of asking Him to do it for you, you will see a dramatic change in the results you get when you pray.

NOTE TO LEADER: *Now would be a great time to ask if any of your students have any pain or sickness in their bodies that they would like prayer for. It's simple: Speak directly to the problem, believe that God has already provided for their healing, and expect to see results.*

Additional Resources:

1. *The Believer's Authority* is a six-part audio teaching available to listen to or download for free at www.awmi.net/extra/audio/1045.

2. *The Believer's Authority,* a book by Andrew Wommack, reveals the spiritual significance of your choices, words, and actions and how they affect your ability to stand against the attacks of Satan and receive God's best. Discover the powerful truths behind real spiritual authority and begin seeing real results. It is available through bookstores or the online store at www.awmi.net/store/usa/books/327.

3. *Don't Limit God* is an empowering five-part audio teaching that reveals how we limit God in our lives and what we can do to break free from our self-imposed limitations. It is available to listen to or download for free at www.awmi.net/extra/audio/1060.

4. *Spiritual Authority* is a six-part audio teaching that takes the cover off of Satan's deception and shows you the power that God has committed to you. Watch your faith soar and your situation improve as you receive the truths of your spiritual authority in Christ. It is available to listen to or download for free at www.awmi. net/extra/audio/1017.

A Better Way to Pray
Lesson 10

Ask, and it shall be given you; seek, and ye shall find; knock, and it shall be opened unto you: For every one that asketh receiveth; and he that seeketh findeth; and to him that knocketh it shall be opened.

MATTHEW 7:7-8

"God is with us all the time. We can spend the entire day in the presence of the Lord. Instead of only setting aside certain times for prayer, we can be in communion with God constantly" (Sharper Than a Two-Edged Sword, Chapter 10).

1. What is prayer?

   A.   First, let me say what prayer is not. It's not something we do for recognition, and it's not a vain repetition we use to gain favor with God or fulfill a religious requirement.

       Prayer is just communication and relationship with God. Communication implies that you listen and hear God speaking to you. Jesus has confirmed that His sheep hear His voice (John 10:27), and the Word says that the children of God are led by His Spirit (Rom. 8:14). But communicating with God doesn't mean hearing an audible voice from heaven.

       Even meditation, or what you are thinking, can be prayer. Scripture says, **"Give ear to my words, O LORD, consider my meditation. Hearken unto the voice of my cry, my King, and my God: for unto thee will I pray"** (Ps. 5:1-2). Not all prayer needs to be spoken; it can be the meditation of your heart.

       The majority of prayer time should be spent communing with God, praising Him, worshiping Him, thanking Him for all He has done, and speaking in tongues. Speaking in tongues is a powerful form of prayer. It draws the wisdom in our spirits out into our understanding, and it allows our spirits to give thanks to God without the limitations of human language or thought (1 Cor. 14:17). It edifies us (1 Cor. 14:5), and it builds up our faith (Jude 20).

2. How many different kinds of prayer are there?

A.   Prayer is more than just asking God to meet your needs. I've already covered that prayer is just communication and relationship with God. There are, however, several different kinds of prayer.

To begin with, New Testament prayer is very different from Old Testament prayer. This makes sense because the Old Testament was looking forward to a time when God would bring salvation, and the New Testament is looking back on Jesus' finished work of redemption. Old Testament prayers show people, such as Abraham or Moses, acting as mediators between God and humanity. But now that Jesus has dealt with sin, Jesus is the *only* mediator between God and man (1 Tim. 2:5). Other men and women can no longer operate as mediators, and anyone attempting to do so is denying the full scope of what Jesus accomplished on the cross.

Other means of prayer include worship, praise, petition, meditation, exercising authority, and agreement. Worshiping and praising God helps you focus on God instead of your circumstances (I discuss the full benefit of worship and praise during the **Lesson** "Staying Full of God"). Meditation on the Word and the principles of God are how you renew your mind (Rom. 12:1-2). Exercising authority is how you enforce, by faith, the promises Jesus has already provided for in His redemptive work (e.g., Mark 11:24). The prayer of agreement is when you know God's power is at work in your situation but maybe you haven't seen a full manifestation yet, so you pray with another believer and agree in prayer with someone that God is working and a manifestation is coming (Matt. 18:18-20).

In terms of praying for the lost, people aren't born again by prayer—they have to hear the Word of God (Rom. 10:14-17). You can share the Gospel with them, or you can pray for laborers to come across their path (Matt. 9:38) to minister the Gospel to them. If the person has heard the Gospel in the past, you can also pray for the Holy Spirit to bring it back to their remembrance. (This type of prayer needs to be repeated because the lost person can reject the help God sends their way.)

Still, you should avoid the mistake of begging God to save the lost, because He desires the lost to be saved more than you do. God has already provided for salvation, it's a finished work, and He has commanded you to go make disciples (e.g., Matt. 28:18-20).

3. How often and for how long should I pray?

A.   A man once came to my office and asked me how much I prayed. As I was considering the question and trying to quantify how much I prayed every day, the Lord spoke to me. My wife and I had spent the entire previous day together.

We weren't talking the whole time, but we were together doing different things. We ate together, drove in the car together, and had a great day.

The Lord asked me, "How much time did you spend with Jamie yesterday?"

The whole day, I thought.

Then the Lord said, "I'm available twenty-four hours a day. Why reduce the time that you communicate with me down to thirty minutes or an hour?"

My wife and I would have a sorry relationship if I ignored her when we were together, eating dinner, driving in the car, and being in the same room without ever acknowledging that she was there. God is with us all the time. *We can spend the entire day in the presence of the Lord.* Instead of only setting aside certain times for prayer, we can be in communion with God constantly.

I have developed a lifestyle of keeping my mind focused on the Lord regardless of what I'm doing. Even when I'm busy making television programs, I'm still listening to the Lord. God speaks to me and reminds me of things, and I'm constantly in communion with Him—that's what prayer is.

4. In what ways is God going to speak to me?

A. Jesus said, **"My sheep hear my voice, and I know them, and they follow me"** (John 10:27). We are God's sheep, and we *can* hear His voice—if we listen.

The primary means that God uses to speak to His people is through His Word. Unless you are seeking to follow the general will of God that is revealed in His Word, He probably isn't going to give you a specific word about your life or situation. (The first steps in following God's will are all revealed in the Word, so He isn't going to show you step 100 by a specific word if you aren't trying to follow step 1.) The number-one way God is going to speak to you is through the Word and by bringing Scripture alive as you pray and meditate on it.

If you have made yourself a living sacrifice and you are renewing your mind, then God will also lead you by peace (Col. 3:15)—*but that's a big "if."* If you haven't done those things, then you can't trust your sense of peace, because you might have "peace" about doing something that is totally carnal and against God. You can't be guided by God's peace if you are saturated with the world. But if you aren't trying to run your own life and you are renewing your mind, then God will often lead you by giving you peace about a direction or by taking peace away.

It's not difficult to have God lead you. You just love Him with your whole heart and commit your life to Him, and when you really delight in the Lord,

He'll start putting His desires in your heart (Ps. 37:4). Then you start moving toward attaining those desires, and when you come to a fork in the road, you follow the peace that's in your heart. It's really pretty simple.

B. God can also speak to you through other people, both by godly counsel and by the gifts of the Holy Spirit. However, you should always compare words of wisdom and words of knowledge against the Word of God to make sure they line up. You also shouldn't be guided solely by what others say; you need to hear from God yourself (Rom. 8:14). I believe that words of wisdom and knowledge usually come as a confirmation of something you already know God has been speaking to you.

C. I have three separate audio teachings (five hours each)—*How to* Find *God's Will*, *How to* Follow *God's Will*, and *How to* Fulfill *God's Will*—that are available to download for free on our website (see "Additional Resources" at the end of this **Lesson**). I recommend these teachings for further study on the topic of hearing God's voice and following His leading through life.

5. Can you recall an instance when you felt God was trying to tell you something? Did you listen?

A. Whether it was buying a house, engaging in a business deal, or trusting someone we shouldn't have, we all know the feeling of saying, "I *knew* I shouldn't have done that!" Something inside was telling us not to do it, but all of the natural evidence suggested it was a good idea, so we went ahead and did it anyway. Then, when everything fell apart, we said, "I *knew* it!" That "sense" of leading is the loss of peace that God sometimes uses to guide us. We need to learn to trust that peace and not be led by the circumstances in our lives.

6. Does God answer all of my prayers?

A. The Scripture says, **"For all the promises of God in him are yea, and in him Amen, unto the glory of God by us"** (2 Cor. 1:20). If God promised it, He'll do it. It's impossible for God to lie (Heb. 6:18), and He will not go back on His Word (Ps. 89:34). So, if God has promised it, He'll make it good (Num. 23:19).

The Word says, **"For the eyes of the LORD run to and fro throughout the whole earth, to shew himself strong in the behalf of them whose heart is perfect toward him"** (2 Chr. 16:9). God is continuously looking for faithful men and women who will take Him at His Word and believe for Him to come through on a promise. As Jesus said, **"If thou canst believe, all things are possible to him that believeth"** (Mark 9:23)

B. Faith can only appropriate what Jesus provided in the atonement. The **Lesson** "Living in the Balance of Grace and Faith" goes into more detail on this subject.

7. Can you remember times when you avoided prayer? Why?

A. If you are avoiding God or prayer out of a sense of unworthiness or shame, then you are probably still relating to God through a performance-based acceptance. Remember, relationship with God is something you receive; it isn't something you earn. You start living holy as a result of having a relationship with God, not as a means of obtaining it.

Paul wrote in his letter to the Romans,

> **But God commendeth his love toward us, in that, while we were yet sinners, Christ died for us. Much more then, being now justified by his blood, we shall be saved from wrath through him. For if, when we were enemies, we were reconciled to God by the death of his Son, much more, being reconciled, we shall be saved by his life. And not only so, but we also joy in God through our Lord Jesus Christ, by whom we have now received the atonement.**
>
> **ROMANS 8-11**

The war is over, you have been reconciled to God by the blood of Jesus, and sin is no longer an issue in your relationship with God. There is no need to feel ashamed or to avoid God—He knows everything and He still loves you. God is looking at you according to your spirit that was made new when you were born again (2 Cor. 5:17), not according to your flesh. Prayer should be the first thing you seek if you have made a poor choice, because repentance and being still in the presence of God brings refreshing (Acts 3:19).

8. Can the devil stop God from hearing my prayers? Can the devil stop me from hearing God? How?

A. Every born-again believer is the temple of the Holy Spirit (1 Cor. 6:19). God lives in you, so you don't need your prayer to get above your nose. It is true that you have an Enemy, but the devil can't stop you from communicating with God. The devil can't stop you from hearing God either—but you can harden your heart and become desensitized to God's voice.

Jesus defeated Satan, and all believers *have been* (past tense) delivered from the powers of darkness (Col. 1:13). You are seated in heavenly places with

Christ Jesus (Eph. 2:6). The Enemy's lies are the only thing you are still fighting against. So, the only power the devil has over you is the power you give him by believing his lies over the Word of God—but God can help you tear those lies down too (2 Cor. 10:3-5).

9. How does my born-again spirit make prayer different for me than it was before I was born again?

A. The purpose of prayer is simply relationship with God. It is fellowship and communion with Him. There are times when we have to use the authority God has given us and command sickness or obstacles to flee, but mostly, prayer is about building relationship with God. It is an opportunity for us to spend time with our heavenly Father and to be further transformed into His image.

God is always present, and the blood of Jesus has made it possible for born-again believers to enter into the holy of holies (Heb. 10:19). The veil has been torn in two, and the obstacles that separated mankind from God under the Old Covenant have been removed. Now believers can enter boldly into the throne room of God and soak in His presence.

Additional Resources:

1. *A Better Way to Pray* is a five-part audio teaching available to listen to or download for free at www.awmi.net/extra/audio/1042.

2. *A Better Way to Pray*, a book by Andrew Wommack, addresses a better way to pray if you're not getting the results you desire. It is available through bookstores or the AWM online store at www.awmi.net/store/usa/books/321.

3. *How to Become a Water Walker: Lessons in Faith* is a three-part audio teaching available to listen to or download for free at www.awmi.net/extra/audio/1037.

4. *How to* Find *God's Will* is a five-part audio teaching available to listen to or download for free at www.awmi.net/extra/audio/1066.

5. *How to* Follow *God's Will* is a five-part audio teaching available to listen to or download for free at www.awmi.net/extra/audio/1067.

6. *How to* Fulfill *God's Will* is a five-part audio teaching available to listen to or download for free at www.awmi.net/extra/audio/1068.

7. *Hebrews Highlights* is a five-part audio teaching that explains the difference in the approach to prayer under the New Covenant versus the Old Covenant. Most believers haven't understood the difference. They still mix the Old with the New, and it's the reason they aren't victorious. Hebrews was written to address this issue. This teaching is available to listen to or download for free at www.awmi.net/extra/audio/1061.

The Effects of Praise
Lesson 11

I will bless the LORD at all times: his praise shall continually be in my mouth.

PSALM 34:1

"You can check your spiritual pulse by examining how thankful you are. The amount of time you spend praising God is the greatest single indicator of where you are in your relationship with the Lord" (Sharper Than a Two-Edged Sword, Chapter 11).

1. **What exactly does my level of thanksgiving, or praise, say about my relationship with God?**

   A. You can check your spiritual pulse by examining how thankful you are. The amount of time you spend praising God is the greatest single indicator of where you are in your relationship with the Lord. Anyone who isn't praising God and operating in thanksgiving—regardless of what is going in their life—doesn't really understand what God has done for them. Most people are content to praise God when things are going well, but their praise stops when the stress of life starts pressing in. Yet times of conflict are when they should be praising God the most. Praise builds faith, runs off the devil, and ministers to God.

   Praise shouldn't be the caboose that follows the circumstances in your life. It should be the engine driving your life. Praise will take you places. It will change your circumstances. Scripture says, **"As ye have therefore received Christ Jesus the Lord, so walk ye in him: Rooted and built up in him, and stablished in the faith, as ye have been taught, abounding therein with thanksgiving"** (Col. 2:6-7).

2. **How will praise build my faith?**

   A. The Word says to praise God because it makes you focus on what God says, rather than on your problems. If the doctor tells you that you are terminally ill, remember that the Word says to give thanks in all circumstances. Start praising God and it will redirect your attention to God's will for you and build your faith to receive a miracle.

Your life is going in the direction of your dominant thoughts. Whatever you think about and focus your attention on determines the course of your life. The trail of thoughts that focuses on the circumstances around you only leads to discouragement. Focusing on your circumstances is only going to hinder faith. Praise, on the other hand, will establish you in faith. It will draw on God's power and allow you to receive the provision that Jesus purchased for you on the cross.

3. Why does praise run off the devil?

    A. Jesus said, **"Yea; have ye never read, Out of the mouth of babes and sucklings thou hast perfected praise?"** (Matt. 21:16). The Scripture also says, **"Out of the mouth of babes and sucklings hast thou ordained strength because of thine enemies, that thou mightest still the enemy and the avenger"** (Ps. 8:2).

    These two scriptures together show us that *praise is strength to still the Enemy and the Avenger*. The reason for this has to do with why Satan transgressed against God in the first place. Isaiah the prophet tells us that Satan was envious of God because he wanted for himself the praise that God was receiving (Is. 14:13-14). Pride made Satan want to be like God. I believe the reason that praise affects the devil so powerfully is because when we praise God, it rubs the devil's nose in what he has always wanted but will never get. It's like taunting the devil and it infuriates him. He is jealous of God, and when you start giving God praise, it drives the devil crazy. He can't stand to hear God praised. It makes him mad and he flees.

4. Does God really want me to praise Him when everything in life seems to be going wrong?

    A. Praising God puts to flight all of the hurts, pains, and demonic oppression that Satan has tried to bind you up with. It opens up your heart and prepares you to receive from God. One of the classic examples of this is when Paul and Silas were beaten and thrown into prison in Philippi. After whipping them, the jailer threw them in the inner dungeon and put their feet in stocks. At midnight, Paul and Silas began to pray and sing praises unto God (Acts 16:25). Suddenly, there was a great earthquake, and all of the prisoners' doors opened and their chains dropped off.

    When the miracle came, Paul and Silas didn't quit praising God, and they didn't run out of the prison. The jailer assumed everyone had escaped and was about to take his own life, but Paul called out for him to stop because all of the prisoners were still there. The greatest miracle here is that none of the other criminals fled. They were so affected by the praise and the power of God that they would rather stay in prison where the anointing of God was than take advantage of the situation and flee.

This shows that Paul and Silas didn't praise God just to get out of their chains. They praised God because they were in love with Him. Their love for God drove them to praise Him—even though their backs were bleeding and they had been thrown in prison unjustly.

Praise is powerful and it releases the anointing of God. God inhabits the praises of His people (Ps. 22:3), and when you start praising Him, it draws the power and the anointing of the Lord into manifestation. Praise will break your chains, drive the devil off, and get you out of bad situations.

5. How can my prayers possibly minister to God?

A. God is the Almighty, but that doesn't mean we can't do something that ministers to Him. Jesus had needs while He was on earth, and many people ministered to Him by doing things such as cooking and caring for Him. God is love, and love likes to be reciprocated. God loved us so much that He gave His only Son to die for us, to bring us back into proper relationship with Him. Our praise is a thanksgiving that lets God know how much we appreciate what He has done for us. It reciprocates the love that He first loved us with, and it ministers to Him.

Many Old Testament scriptures exhorted Israel to "bless the Lord." This has become a religious cliché today. Now people say "Bless the Lord" all the time, but the words themselves are not necessarily a blessing to God. Blessing the Lord is saying, "Father, I love You. Thank You that You are a good God. Thank You for moving in my life." Thanking God is what blesses Him.

God has emotions. He isn't bound by His emotions the way that people are, but He has them. It ministers to God when we give Him praise. God gave everything for us. The least we can do is be thankful. In our own lives, we like to be thanked when we go out of our way to do something for somebody else. It's nice when someone acknowledges what we've done and says thank you. Praise is simply a way of thanking God for all He has done.

Additional Resources:

1. *The Effects of Praise* is a three-part audio teaching available to listen to or download for free at www.awmi.net/extra/audio/1004.

2. *The Effects of Praise,* a book by Andrew Wommack, shows how the single act of praise begins to harvest peace, joy, pleasure, and contentment into every area of your life! Through praise, you can finally overcome anxiety, depression, and stress in your life. It is available through bookstores or the AWM online store at www.awmi.net/store/usa/books/309.

3. *How to Stay Positive in a Negative World* is a five-part audio teaching. If you watch the news, read the newspaper, or listen to the negative conversations of those around you long enough, you'll find yourself discouraged. This teaching will show you how to rise above the noise of negativity and live your life according to the promises of God's Word. It is available to listen to or download for free at www.awmi.net/extra/audio/1065.

4. "Ministering unto God" is an audio teaching available to listen to or download for free at www.awmi.net/extra/audio/general.

Harnessing Your Emotions
Lesson 12

> **Rejoice evermore. Pray without ceasing. In every thing give thanks: for this is the will of God in Christ Jesus concerning you.**
>
> **1 THESSALONIANS 5:16-18**

"Out-of-control emotions make life miserable. As believers, we can't afford to let emotions run our lives" (Sharper Than a Two-Edged Sword, Chapter 12).

1. Are emotions an automatic response to what happens to me in life, or do I have some control over them?

A. Most people feel completely powerless to prevent negative emotions from dominating them. They don't realize that they have authority over their emotions, and it is within their power to harness them. The Word of God tells us, **"Rejoice evermore. Pray without ceasing. In every thing give thanks: for this is the will of God in Christ Jesus concerning you"** (1 Thess. 5:16-18).

This is just one of many scriptures that tell us to rejoice in all circumstances. God wouldn't have commanded us to control our emotions if we couldn't do it. The simple fact that we are commanded to rejoice and to praise God at all times is proof that we can.

God says we can harness our emotions, but popular culture encourages us to do the exact opposite. Psychologists tell people not to hold anything back. They say we have to vent and let it all out. This viewpoint has its roots in the false assumption that our emotional state is an automatic response to the things that are happening to us in life. The idea is that we can't do anything to prevent emotion from rising up and controlling us, so we might as well let it all loose. But that isn't true. I don't deny that we can be hurt or that we have negative emotional reactions to upsetting circumstances, but we can deny those emotions the opportunity to rule our lives.

2. What is the difference between experiencing negative emotions in reaction to a situation and allowing those emotions to rule my life?

A. Those who say that emotional responses to circumstances are inevitable and that you can't stop those emotions from controlling you have wrongly reduced human beings to mere machines. You aren't a machine, and you didn't evolve from fish or animals. You were created in the image of God, and you have a "spirit man" on the inside of you that gives you the capacity to operate above the animal level. You aren't reduced to just responding to stimuli from your environment. Your born-again spirit gives you the ability to live supernaturally.

I remember an instance when I was working with a ministry in Charlotte, North Carolina, feeding some homeless people. I was talking to an alcoholic, and he got so mad that he spit a big glob of tobacco juice right in my face. Initially, I was mad. For a fraction of a second, I wanted to punch his lights out, but I didn't. I knew that Jesus loved him, and I knew that I had love, joy, and peace abiding in my born-again spirit (Gal. 5:22). So, I denied anger the privilege of retaliating. I wiped the spit from my face and kept on preaching. I didn't miss a beat. I just kept telling him about how much God loved him, and I was able to operate from my born-again spirit rather than from my emotions.

3. What is the fruit of the Holy Spirit?

A. The fruit of the Holy Spirit is listed in Paul's letter to the Galatians: **"But the fruit of the Spirit is love, joy, peace, longsuffering, gentleness, goodness, faith, Meekness, temperance: against such there is no law"** (Gal. 5:22-23).

The *English Standard Version* says, **"But the fruit of the Spirit is love, joy, peace, patience, kindness, goodness, faithfulness, gentleness, self-control; against such things there is no law."**

4. Do I have the fruit of the Holy Spirit all of the time, or only when I feel it emotionally?

A. The fruit of the Holy Spirit is being produced in our spirits continuously and simultaneously because all born-again believers are the temple of the Holy Spirit and the Holy Spirit resides in us (1 Cor. 3:16). There are nine fruits listed in Galatians. They are all produced at the same time, and together they add up to the *fruit* (singular) of the Holy Spirit. We constantly possess the fruit of the Holy Spirit regardless of whether or not we can feel it in our souls.

5. How is sin conceived in my emotions?

A. The Bible says,

> **Let no man say when he is tempted, I am tempted of God: for God cannot be tempted with evil, neither tempteth he any man: But every man is tempted, when he is drawn away of his own lust, and enticed.**

**Then when lust hath conceived, it bringeth forth sin:
and sin, when it is finished, bringeth forth death.**

JAMES 1:13-15

People today narrowly define "lust" as illicit sexual desire for another person, and it is used that way in Scripture. However, it also means to long for or desire. The meaning of lust in this scripture is "desire." All people are tempted when they are lured away and enticed by their own *desires*, and then when desire (or emotions) conceive, it brings forth sin. Here's the point: Emotions aren't a byproduct of people's environments; emotions are where sin is conceived.

The picture of sin being conceived and then giving birth to death is a mirror of the natural process of conception and childbirth. A woman conceives a child, and approximately forty weeks later, she gives birth. In the same way, once sin is conceived in your emotions, it will ultimately give birth to death. You can't see it right away, and it might take time, but sin will eventually give birth to death. It's pretty simple: Sexual relations lead to conception, which leads to childbirth. In the natural realm, if a man and a woman don't want to conceive a child, they shouldn't have sexual relations. It works the same way in the spiritual realm: If you don't want to sin, then don't conceive sin in your emotions.

6. **Why shouldn't I just let my emotions run wild when something bad happens? Won't releasing all of that pressure help me deal better with the situation?**

   A.   Every time you allow negative emotions to run amuck, you are conceiving sin. The problem is, you may not recognize or feel any responsibility for that conception. You are letting your desires and emotions run wild, but then when the birth of sin and death starts to show, you don't want any part of it. Essentially, you have allowed the conception of sin in your emotions, and now that you are nine months pregnant, you don't want to have a child. It doesn't work that way. You don't try to stop the birth—you stop conception. If there is a strong fight inside of you, pulling you toward sin, it's because you have already conceived the sin in your emotions. Stop the conception and you won't have to worry about giving birth.

   Sin doesn't come on you like the flu; it has to be conceived. You don't commit adultery accidentally; it first has to be conceived in your emotions. It begins by you allowing yourself to desire someone other than your spouse—that's the conception. It could be something as small as dreaming about the way some television character treats his or her spouse, and then beginning to indulge fantasies and live vicariously. You might think there isn't anything wrong with that. You might think that since you aren't actually *doing* anything, there is no harm in it. You feel no accountability toward controlling your emotions.

I don't mean to be offensive, but in a spiritual sense, every time you indulge negative emotions, it's like having spiritual intercourse with the devil. The devil is planting a seed on the inside of you that is going to grow into a sin, which eventually brings destruction. If you would recognize that, I guarantee it would change the way that you look at indulging emotions.

7. How can I prevent negative emotions from running away with me?

A. Instead of allowing depression and discouragement and other negative emotions to overrule you, recognize that the Bible tells you to be strong and of good courage in the face of trying circumstances (Josh. 1:9). In many places, the Word of God commands you to harness your emotions. Every time you disobey that command and allow yourself to slip into negative emotions, it's like having a spiritual affair with the devil. You know you shouldn't feel that way, but you feel like you can't help it, so you give in. Giving up, or giving in, is going to plant a seed on the inside of you that will bring forth something you don't want. When the birth comes around, you're going to be crying out for God to save you.

The night Jesus was betrayed, He told the disciples, **"Let not your heart be troubled: ye believe in God, believe also in me"** (John 14:1). **"Let not your heart be troubled"** is a command, not a suggestion. Jesus didn't say, *"Try* not to let your hearts be troubled."

I believe it is significant that the very first thing He told them to do was to harness their emotions. In my experience, with myself and in dealing with others in crisis, I have found that the reaction to the initial moments of a crisis is vital. If you fall apart like a two-dollar suitcase at the very beginning—if you let fear, despair, grief, and sorrow overwhelm you—it's nearly impossible to overcome those emotions and walk in faith later on. It's a lot easier to stop those emotions from ever entering in than it is to try to keep them from getting out after you have been entertaining them.

Over the years, I've had several horses, and I can tell you that if you let a horse run away with you, it is nearly impossible to rein it in. It is very difficult to overcome a horse's runaway momentum. On the other hand, I've taught a seven-year-old boy how to control a relatively wild horse by following a few simple instructions. He rode my horse for nearly two hours without any problems. Shortly after the seven year old dismounted my horse, a twenty-year-old man showed up at my place, wanting to ride. By contrast, the young man didn't want to listen to any of my instructions. Within minutes, the horse took off running, and he couldn't stop it. Eventually, the horse threw the young man off, and he ended up making a trip to the hospital.

Emotions are like horses: It's a lot easier to keep them in check than it is to rein them in after they have begun to run wild. If you fall to pieces the moment something bad happens, it's going to be a lot harder to pull yourself back together and start believing God for a miracle. It's much easier to harness your emotions from the start. Thankfully, God has given you the power to do so.

Additional Resources:

1. *Harnessing Your Emotions* is a four-part audio teaching available to listen to or download for free at www.awmi.net/extra/audio/1005.

2. *Harnessing Your Emotions*, a book by Andrew Wommack, will give you a look at who you are in Christ that very few Christians have seen of themselves. This is life-changing information and one of the major keys to a victorious life in Christ. It is available through bookstores or the AWM online store at www.awmi.net/store/usa/books/313.

3. *Anger Management* is a three-part audio teaching in which Andrew shares truths from God's Word on the subject of anger that are as rare as gold. It is available to listen to or download for free at www.awmi.net/extra/audio/1044.

4. *God's Kind of Love Through You* is a nine-part audio teaching. Once you understand how much God loves you, it will compel you to allow God's love to flow through you. However, there are many misunderstandings about what that means and how to do it. This series will help. It is available to listen to or download for free at www.awmi.net/extra/audio/1055.

Staying Full of God
Lesson 13

Because that, when they knew God, they glorified him not as God, neither were thankful; but became vain in their imaginations, and their foolish heart was darkened.

ROMANS 1:21

"This passage of Scripture describes four progressive steps that people take to harden their hearts toward God. We can discover the keys to staying full of God simply by turning those steps around and doing the opposite" (Sharper Than a Two-Edged Sword, Chapter 13).

1. **What are the four steps to staying full of God?**

   A. In order, the steps are—

      i. Glorifying God and what He has done in your life

      ii. Thankfulness

      iii. Having a positive imagination

      iv. Keeping a good heart (making sure that the Word of God is the dominant influence in your heart—not the world, your circumstances, etc.)

2. **Does the power of God leak out of my spirit over time, making it necessary for me to get a refill?**

   A. No, I don't think that encounters with God come with an expiration date, and then you need to go get a new dose of the Holy Spirit. My personal experience is completely contrary to that.

      For some people, experiences with God may seem to lose their initial strength over time, but it has nothing to do with God withdrawing His presence. It isn't because there is an expiration date on the power He releases in their lives. Their own actions are what decrease the effectiveness of God's touch in their lives. It's what they do, not what God does.

      Neglecting God is what causes people to feel like leaky vessels.

3. **Why can't I value and esteem the opinions of others as well as what God thinks about me?**

   A.   Misplaced values diminish the impact God has in your life, and sometimes you may place a higher value on circumstances, or the opinions of others, than you do on God. Your attention works like a magnifying glass: Whatever you focus on gets bigger, and whatever you neglect diminishes. If you focus on the Word of God, then the Lord will take on greater importance in your life. Whereas focusing on the opinions of others will cause your understanding of God's view of you to shrink by comparison.

   It's like a seesaw or a pair of scales: Both ends can't be up at the same time. You can't truly value what God is saying about you and value what other people are saying at the same time.

4. **Why do the things that other people say or think about me get under my skin?**

   A.   One day, as I was hiking up Pikes Peak with a friend, he began telling me some things that another friend of ours was saying about us behind our backs. It doesn't bless me to hear other people criticizing me, but I don't focus on it, because it diminishes the value I place on what God has said about me. So, I said to him, "Look, I don't want to hear it. I know what he thinks of me, and I just don't want to hear it anymore."

   My friend was quiet for a while, and then he said, "Why doesn't what he is saying bother you, like it bothers me?"

   "Because I don't value his opinion as much as you do," I answered.

   The things that other people say will only really upset you if you esteem their opinion. I'm not saying you shouldn't value what anybody else says—especially if you live with them—but in comparison with the value you place on God's Word, nobody else's opinion should matter.

5. **What can I do to make my problems seem smaller and the solution bigger?**

   A.   As I've mentioned, your attention works like a magnifying glass: Whatever you focus on gets bigger, and whatever you neglect diminishes. If you spend your time thinking about and meditating on your problems, your focus is going to magnify the very thing you are trying to overcome. Focusing on your problems can make a small issue seem like an insurmountable hurdle.

   On the other hand, you can use your focus to your advantage by thinking about and meditating on the Word of God. God is always able, but focusing on the Word will make God take on greater significance in your heart. You'll begin to see and believe in God's power to get you over, through, or around the difficulties you are facing. And the problem will shrink in comparison.

6. How does my imagination help or hinder my faith?

A. Imagination is often thought of as something for kids, and adults overlook its importance. But imagination is where people conceive the things of God. Imagination is forming a mental picture of something that isn't real to the senses. People think with pictures. It's how they do anything from giving directions to solving problems, and it is essential to staying full of God.

For instance, you aren't likely to see healing manifest in your body if you imagine yourself as a sick person. If you see yourself sick, that's what you will be. **"As he thinketh in his heart, so is he"** (Prov. 23:7), so you want your imagination working for you—not against you. In Scripture, hope is the word that is used for a positive imagination that is working in your favor.

7. What role does the Word of God play in helping me stay full of God?

A. The heart is what you live from. It is the ground from which your life grows. Jesus said, **"A good man out of the good treasure of the heart bringeth forth good things: and an evil man out of the evil treasure bringeth forth evil things"** (Matt. 12:35).

Your behavior and words spring forth from your heart, so staying full of God means having a heart that is filled with the Word of God. You should only imagine yourself as God sees you. If the Word of God has established in your heart who He says you are, live that image out. The Word of God is the seed you must plant in your heart if you want to see God's love grow and bear fruit in your life.

Additional Resources:

1. *Discover the Keys to Staying Full of God* is a four-part audio teaching available to listen to or download for free at www.awmi.net/extra/audio/1029.

2. *Discover the Keys to Staying Full of God*, a book by Andrew Wommack, reveals the essentials to a strong, close relationship with God. It is available through bookstores or the AWM online store at www.awmi.net/store/usa/books/324.

3. *Don't Limit God* is a five-part audio teaching. Most Christians believe that God, in His sovereignty, does what He wants on earth. Is that true, or is it possible that He has limited Himself by His own words? If He has, then maybe the only limits in your life have been placed there by you. Combine this understanding with this **Lesson**, "Staying Full of God," and watch the limits in your life fade away. It is available to listen to or download for free at www.awmi.net/extra/audio/1060.

God Wants You Well
Lesson 14

> **That it might be fulfilled which was spoken by [Isaiah] the prophet, saying, Himself took our infirmities, and bare our sicknesses.**
>
> **MATTHEW 8:17, BRACKETS MINE**

"Jesus took our infirmities and bore our sicknesses in His body on the cross. It is a part of the atonement of the Lord Jesus Christ for us to be healed. Jesus doesn't want us to be sick any more than He wants us to sin" (Sharper Than a Two-Edged Sword, Chapter 14)

1. **How do I know it is God's will for me to be well?**

   A. The Bible says of Jesus, **"Who being the brightness of his glory, and the express image of his person, and upholding all things by the word of his power, when he had by himself purged our sins, sat down on the right hand of the Majesty on high"** (Heb. 1:3).

   Jesus is the perfect representation of God the Father (Heb. 1:3). Jesus said that He only did what He saw His Father do (John 5:19), and He told His disciples that to see Him was to see the Father (John 14:9). Jesus represented God perfectly, so if we want to know God's will concerning healing, all we have to do is examine the life and teachings of Jesus.

   Jesus never caused anyone to be sick, and He didn't use sickness to teach people lessons. Yet today, people are saying God has "blessed" them with sickness because it captured their attention and drew them to the Lord. People are crediting God with making them paralyzed or ill, but Jesus never used illness to accomplish His will. Sickness is never a "blessing in disguise"; it's listed as part of the curse (Deut. 28:15-68).

   There is not a single example in Scripture of Jesus doing the things that religion is blaming God for today. Jesus said, **"He that hath seen me hath seen the Father."** One of the greatest testimonies in Scripture that God wants you well is the fact that Jesus' life expressly shows His desire to heal the sick.

   When the Apostle Peter was preaching the Gospel to the Gentile household of Cornelius, he summarized the life and ministry of Jesus by saying, **"How God anointed Jesus of Nazareth with the Holy Ghost and with** power: who went about doing good, and healing all that were oppressed of the devil; for God was with him" (Acts 10:38).

It says that Jesus **"went about doing good."** Not only did Jesus heal those who were oppressed of the devil; He healed them *all*. He didn't just go around healing some people. Jesus' actions are a demonstration of God's will to heal everyone, not just a select few.

2. Do the scriptures about healing apply to my body, or just to my soul and spirit?

A. Jesus, out of His great love, took our sin *and* our sicknesses upon His body on the cross. The Word of God is very clear on this point:

> **Surely he hath borne our griefs, and carried our sorrows: yet we did esteem him stricken, smitten of God, and afflicted. But he was wounded for our transgressions, he was bruised for our iniquities: the chastisement of our peace was upon him; and with his stripes we are healed.**
>
> **ISAIAH 53:4-5**

This bold declaration clearly says that by the stripes of Jesus, we are healed. Religion enters in with its customary confusion and tries to spiritualize this scripture by saying we are only healed in our hearts. Religion says this means that in our hearts and emotions, we were healed from the hurt and the pain of sin. It is true to say that, but it isn't the whole truth. Yes, Jesus came to set us free emotionally and spiritually, but He didn't stop there.

This scripture also applies to the healing of our physical bodies. The Gospel of Matthew tells how the people brought their sick to Jesus, and He healed them *all* (showing His desire to heal everyone). Then it references this exact prophecy, saying, **"That it might be fulfilled which was spoken by Esaias the prophet, saying, Himself took our infirmities, and bare our sicknesses"** (Matt. 8:17).

Jesus took our infirmities and bore our sicknesses in His body on the cross. It is a part of the atonement of the Lord Jesus Christ for us to be healed. Jesus doesn't want us to be sick any more than He wants us to sin.

3. If it's God's will for us to be well, then why doesn't everyone get healed?

A. Some get confused about God's will to heal when they see Christians die of sickness, even some who believed God would heal them. Religion concludes that it must not have been God's will to heal in those cases, rather than accepting the possibility that healing was available but, for some reason, those people weren't able to reach out and take advantage of it. Rather than risk hurting anyone's feelings or accepting any responsibility, religion places the blame on God.

I don't know why everyone who believes for healing isn't healed, but I know it isn't God's fault. Whatever unanswered questions we have about healing do not change the fact that the express will of God, as seen in the life of Jesus and written in the Word, is that God wants you well. Jesus paid for sickness in His atonement so you can be well, and untold numbers of people are being healed by the power of God all over the world today.

4. What does it mean to be double minded, and how does it impact my ability to receive from God?

A. Double-mindedness is being partially focused on the truth of God and partially focused on your circumstances or the influences of the world. It means to be of two minds on a matter—to have your thoughts, focus, and attention divided between opposing positions.

To effectively resist the devil, you have to understand that God wants you well *when* you pray, because half efforts at resistance won't work. The Bible says,

> **If any of you lack wisdom, let him ask of God, that giveth to all men liberally, and upbraideth not; and it shall be given him. But let him ask in faith, nothing wavering. For he that wavereth is like a wave of the sea driven with the wind and tossed. For let not that man think that he shall receive any thing of the Lord. A double minded man is unstable in all his ways.**
>
> **JAMES 1:5-8**

This principle of not wavering when you petition God isn't limited to requesting wisdom. It can be applied to healing also. You won't receive healing if you are asking God to heal you but at the same time wavering in your heart about whether or not it is His will to heal. That's being double minded, and you won't receive anything that way. You have to believe you receive when you pray (Mark 11:24). In order to believe without wavering when you pray, you have to *know* that God wants you well. It must be settled in your heart.

5. I've heard people say that God used sickness and tragedy in their lives to teach them something. Does God really do that?

A. God is not the author of sickness, and He doesn't use sickness—or any other kind of evil—to accomplish His will. He has nothing whatsoever to do with sickness. James, a leader in the early Jerusalem church, wrote:

> **Let no man say when he is tempted, I am tempted of God: for God cannot be tempted with evil, neither tempteth he any man...Every good gift and every perfect gift is from above, and cometh down from the Father of lights, with whom is no variableness, neither shadow of turning.**
>
> **JAMES 1:13 AND 17**

Wrongly believing that God is behind sickness, pain, and suffering is going to affect your understanding of His love. Associating God with sickness is propaganda from the Enemy. The idea behind propaganda is that if you repeat the lie enough times, people will start believing it. Even if you can see the fallacy, the lie can work its way into your belief system because you start thinking that there must be some truth to something you hear over and over again. Religion mentions that God loves us but then goes on to say that God makes babies sick or gives people cancer because He loves them and wants to teach them something. That isn't love.

Imagine if a man had the power to give people cancer, cause debilitating pain, or inflict babies with deformities. After he had done those things, no one would look to him and suppose he did it out of love. There isn't a civilized nation on the face of the earth that wouldn't prosecute him to the fullest extent of the law. A man such as that would be thrown in prison for criminal behavior. Yet religion is trying to say that God causes tragedy because He loves you. It is a lie that has been repeated so often, people have started believing it.

The destructive power of this lie is that it renders you unable to reconcile the love of God with the use of sickness as a teaching tool. Deep down in your heart, whether you understand it or not, it's going to affect your relationship with God and your understanding of how much He loves you. You can't blame God for causing tragedy in your life and trust Him wholeheartedly at the same time.

Jesus **"went about doing good."** It is good to be well—it's bad to be sick. Sickness is not a blessing from God sent to make you holy. Sickness is an attack from the devil. Sometimes it is completely demonic and spiritual in its origin. other times, it is just the result of living in a fallen world. But sickness and tragedy are never from God.

6. How can confusion over what God is responsible for affect my decisions to submit to some things I should be resisting?

A. Teaching that God uses sickness to accomplish His will causes people to drop their guard and to embrace something that is actually from the devil. Scripture says that those whom Jesus healed were oppressed by the devil, not by God (Acts 10:38). And the Lord's command to us is clear: **"Submit yourselves therefore to God. Resist the devil, and he will flee from you"** (James 4:7).

Some things in life are from God. Other things are from the devil. We are supposed to submit to God and resist the devil. Anyone who wrongly interprets sickness as being from God is submitting to the devil instead of resisting him. It is important to know when to submit and when to resist.

Religion is the source of a lot of confusion. It replaces a vibrant relationship with God, through Jesus, with obeying rules and regulations. In the case of healing, religion teaches that sickness is a blessing in disguise and that God uses it to humble you or make you a better person. It is calling evil good, and good evil (Is. 5:20). In effect, this confusion causes you to embrace the devil and prevents you from receiving healing from God. Obviously, sickness is not going to flee from you as long as you are embracing it. You have to resist the devil in order to make him flee.

7. What are some additional scriptural proofs that demonstrate God's desire for us to be well?

A. God has declared Himself to be our Healer.

    i. **"I will put none of these diseases upon thee, which I have brought upon the Egyptians: for I am the LORD that healeth thee"** (Ex. 15:26). What is translated **"the Lord that healeth thee"** in this scripture is one of the names of God: *Jehovah Rapha*. We're not begging God to be something that He isn't. God calls Himself our Healer, so believing He wants us well is just taking Him at His Word.

B. Jesus took our *sins and* sickness on the cross. It's a finished work, and we've already got it!

    i. **"Surely he hath borne our griefs, and carried our sorrows: yet we did esteem him stricken, smitten of God, and afflicted. But he was wounded for our transgressions, he was bruised for our iniquities: the chastisement of our peace was upon him; and with his stripes we are healed"** (Is. 53:4-5).

    ii. **"That it might be fulfilled which was spoken by Esaias the prophet, saying, Himself took our infirmities, and bare our sicknesses"** (Matt. 8:17). Jesus took and bore (past tense) our sicknesses.

    iii. **"Who his own self bare our sins in his own body on the tree,**

that we, being dead to sins, should live unto righteousness: by whose stripes ye were healed" (1 Pet. 2:24). You *were* healed—past tense.

C.   Jesus was a perfect display of the will of God, and His will to heal hasn't changed.

    i.   **"Who being the brightness of his glory, and the express image of his person, and upholding all things by the word of his power, when he had by himself purged our sins, sat down on the right hand of the Majesty on high"** (Heb. 1:3).

    ii.   **"Jesus Christ the same yesterday, and to day, and for ever"** (Heb. 13:8).

    iii.   **"For I am the LORD, I change not"** (Mal. 3:6)

D.   Jesus healed them ***all***.

    i.   It is mentioned fifteen times in the Gospels that Jesus healed <u>all</u> who were present (Matt 4:23-24, 8:16-17, 9:35, 12:15, 14:14, 34-36, 15:30-31, 19:2, 21:14; Mark 1:32-34, 6:56; Luke 4:40, 6:17-19, 9:11, and 17:12-17). Jesus never refused to heal anyone.

E.   God's Word promises healing, and it is impossible for God to lie.

    i.   **"Beloved, I wish above all things that thou mayest prosper and be in health, even as thy soul prospereth"** (3 John 2).

    ii.   **"Bless the LORD, O my soul, and forget not all his benefits: Who forgiveth all thine iniquities; who healeth all thy diseases"** (Ps. 103:2-3).

    iii.   **"But if the Spirit of him that raised up Jesus from the dead dwell in you, he that raised up Christ from the dead shall also quicken your mortal bodies by his Spirit that dwelleth in you"** (Rom. 8:11).

    iv.   **"He sent his word, and healed them, and delivered them from their destructions"** (Ps. 107:20).

    v.   **"Verily, verily, I say unto you, He that believeth on me, the works that I do shall he do also; and greater works than these shall he do; because I go unto my Father. And whatsoever ye shall ask in my name, that will I do, that the Father may be glorified in the Son. If ye shall ask any thing in my name, I will do it"** (John 14:12-14).

vi. **"For all the promises of God in him are yea, and in him Amen, unto the glory of God by us"** (2 Cor. 1:20).

vii. **"There shall no evil befall thee, neither shall any plague come nigh thy dwelling"** (Ps. 91:10).

viii. **"And ye shall serve the LORD your God, and he shall bless thy bread, and thy water; and I will take sickness away from the midst of thee"** (Ex. 23:25).

ix. **"That by two immutable things, in which it was impossible for God to lie, we might have a strong consolation, who have fled for refuge to lay hold upon the hope set before us"** (Heb. 6:18).

x. **"God is not a man, that he should lie; neither the son of man, that he should repent: hath he said, and shall he not do it? or hath he spoken, and shall he not make it good?"** (Num. 23:19).

xi. **"My covenant will I not break, nor alter the thing that is gone out of my lips"** (Ps. 89:34).

F. Satan is the author of sickness, and Jesus came to destroy the works of the devil.

  i. **"How God anointed Jesus of Nazareth with the Holy Ghost and with power: who went about doing good, and healing all that were oppressed of the devil; for God was with him"** (Acts 10:38).

  ii. **"For this purpose the Son of God was manifested, that he might destroy the works of the devil"** (1 John 3:8).

  iii. **"The thief cometh not, but for to steal, and to kill, and to destroy: I am come that they might have life, and that they might have it more abundantly"** (John 10:10).

G. Jesus has redeemed us from the curse of the Law.

  i. **"Christ hath redeemed us from the curse of the law, being made a curse for us: for it is written, Cursed is every one that hangeth on a tree"** (Gal. 3:13).

     1. Sickness and disease are listed as curses for disobedience to the Law in Deuteronomy 28:15-63. The promises for obedience of the Law are listed in Deuteronomy 28:1-14. The first verse sets the condition for inheriting the promises as obeying the Law, but Jesus has paid the price for us—we don't have to. So, because Jesus hearkened diligently unto the voice of the Father, observed all the commandments, and took all of God's wrath against sin on our behalf, all of these blessings have come upon us.

ii. **"Who hath delivered us from the power of darkness, and hath translated us into the kingdom of his dear Son"** (Col. 1:13).

iii. **"In whom we have redemption through his blood, the forgiveness of sins, according to the riches of his grace"** (Eph. 1:7).

iv. **"For he hath made him to be sin for us, who knew no sin; that we might be made the righteousness of God in him"** (2 Cor. 5:21).

v. **"Ye are of God, little children, and have overcome them: because greater is he that is in you, than he that is in the world"** (1 John 4:4).

H. **What about Paul's thorn in the flesh?**

i. People sometimes recall that the Apostle Paul mentioned a "thorn in the flesh" and cite this as evidence that it isn't God's will to heal or that He will send sickness to keep us humble. But Scripture plainly shows that Paul's thorn was a messenger of Satan, not a sickness or disease:

> **And lest I should be exalted above measure through the abundance of the revelations, there was given to me a thorn in the flesh, the messenger of Satan to buffet me, lest I should be exalted above measure.**
>
> **2 CORINTHIANS 12:7**

Paul went on to speak of the infirmity of the flesh, but he never mentioned sickness. In fact, just before this scripture, Paul listed the trials he had endured as a minister of Christ, and sickness was never mentioned as one of his trials (2 Cor. 11:23-28).

In his letter to the Galatians, Paul mentioned suffering an infirmity of the flesh, but that is no wonder, given how many times he was beaten and tortured! (The word "infirmity" can mean sickness or weakness.) It fact, on one occasion, some Jews stoned Paul until they thought they had killed him and then dragged him outside of town and left him for dead. The disciples stood around Paul until he rose up and went back into the city. The next day, he traveled to Derbe, in the region of Galatia, with Barnabas. The infirmities he spoke about in his letter to the Galatians (Gal. 4:13-15) are likely the result of having been stoned and left for dead—not of any permanent affliction or illness.

Paul's thorn was a messenger of Satan that attacked Paul's ministry efforts, causing him to be beaten, imprisoned, shipwrecked, stoned and left for dead, and in trials and perils often. They were things that came from "without" to attack him (2 Cor. 11:28)—not from within, as sickness.

Additionally, Paul's thorn never hindered him in his tremendous ministry efforts. He said he was the least of the apostles but that he had labored more than any other apostle for the kingdom of God (1 Cor. 15:9-10). He labored more than Peter, James, John, or any of the others. He didn't do that being sick.

Finally, when Paul prayed for God to remove the thorn, the Lord said, **"My grace is sufficient for thee: for my strength is made perfect in weakness"** (2 Cor. 12:9). The Greek word that was translated **"weakness"** here is the same word used for **"infirmities"** in the previous verses and **"infirmity"** in Galatians 4:13. Paul was using this word to describe weakness, not sickness. Sickness is oppression from the devil (Acts 10:38), and God has no part in anything that is evil (James 1:13 and 17). It makes no sense to say that God's strength could be made perfect in sickness. On the other hand, it makes perfect sense that God's strength is fulfilled and completed in weakness because when we are in a state of weakness, it is obvious that God—not the strength of man—is doing the work.

Paul said, **"Therefore I take pleasure in infirmities, in reproaches, in necessities, in persecutions, in distresses for Christ's sake: for when I am weak, then am I strong"** (2 Cor. 12:10). He said this because when Satan attacked his ministry from without (the "thorn") and he should have died or failed but succeeded anyway, it was a testimony that God was laboring with him. God was able to accomplish more through Paul because he understood that unless God was directing and empowering his ministry efforts, his labors wouldn't amount to anything. As the psalmist wrote, **"Except the LORD build the house, they labor in vain that build it"** (Ps. 127:1).

Additional Resources:

1. *Healing Testimonies* are video clips documenting healings that have occurred through some contact with Andrew Wommack Ministries. See the evidence of God working miracles. These stories will encourage you and build your faith. They are available to view free at www.awmi.net/extra/healing.

2. *Healing Journeys* Volumes 1, 2, and 3 are available for purchase through the AWM online store at www.awmi.net/store/usa/videos. Each DVD documents five different stories of the power of God's Word working in the lives of people.

3. *God Wants You Well* is a book by Andrew Wommack where he shares the truth of what God's unconditional love and grace has already provided. Healing is a big part of that provision. Andrew answers many common questions, including those about Paul's thorn in the flesh, the sovereignty of God, and more. If you or someone you know is in need of healing, this book is for you. It is available through bookstores or the AWM online store at www.awmi.net/store/usa/books/330.

4. *God Wants You Well* is a four-part audio teaching available to listen to or download for free at www.awmi.net/extra/audio/1036.

5. "Healing Scriptures" is a collection of healing scriptures with soft background music. As you listen, your mind will be able to relax and your faith will be built to receive your healing. It is available to listen to or download for free at www.awmi.net/extra/audio/i05.

6. *How to Receive a Miracle* is a three-part audio teaching that will show you how to grab a hold of miracles and make them happen. It is available to listen to or download for free at www.awmi.net/extra/audio/1006.

7. *The Good Report: God Wants You Well*, a booklet by Andrew Wommack, is a compilation of articles on the topic of healing. It is available through the AWM online store at www.awmi.net/store/usa/books/102.

Hardness of Heart
Lesson 15

When any one heareth the word of the kingdom, and understandeth it not, then cometh the wicked one, and catcheth away that which was sown in his heart.

MATTHEW 13:19

"Hardening of the heart in one area is a byproduct of what you focus your attention on. Your heart becomes sensitive to what you consider, and it becomes hardened toward the things you aren't meditating on" (Sharper Than a Two-Edged Sword, Chapter 15).

1. **What does the Bible mean when it talks about the "heart"?**

    A.   Usually, the Bible isn't speaking of the physical heart but of your affections and attention. In that sense, the heart is best understood in relation to spirit, soul, and body. It is the gateway to the spirit. It is the meeting place of the spirit and the soul and is the center of thought, action, and feeling. You can think of it like a valve that determines how much of God and your spirit can flow out into your soul, body, and environment.

    If you focus your heart (affections and attention) on the things of God, then the heart valve is open, and the nature of God that is resident in your spirit is able to flow out into your soul and body—for example, bringing healing to your mind, emotions, or physical body. On the other hand, focusing on the things of this world shuts that valve and stops the power of God from flowing out.

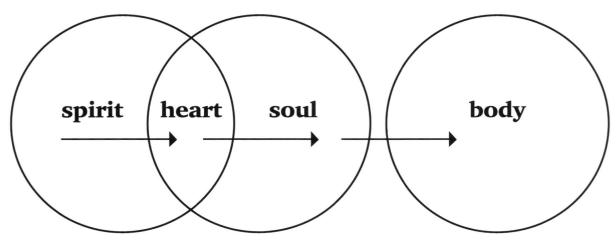

[*Example diagram* showing the relationship of the heart to spirit and soul, and demonstrating the "valve" operation of the heart in opening or shutting off the power of God that potentially flows from the spirit.]

2. What does my heart have to do with my ability to perceive spiritual reality?

A. The Lord made us in such a way that whatever we focus our hearts upon—whatever we delight in—we become sensitive to, and whatever we neglect, we become hardened to. If we are more comfortable with the natural realm than with the spiritual realm, we have hearts that are hardened toward God. We can become sensitive to God and to spiritual reality by focusing our hearts on relationship with God and the Word.

When we have hardened hearts, we see with our physical eyes, but we can't see with our hearts. We have physical ears, but we can't hear the voice of the Lord in our hearts. We can't remember spiritual things. If we are having trouble perceiving, understanding, or remembering the things of God, we have hardened hearts. In simple terms, a hardened heart causes spiritual dullness. It prevents us from functioning the way God intends, and it keeps us from perceiving spiritual truths.

3. How are the things I think about and entertain related to temptation?

A. Your heart becomes sensitive to what you consider, and it becomes hardened toward the things you aren't meditating on. Either you focus your attention on God and become numb to the things of the world, or you focus on the cares of this world and become inattentive to God. In both cases, the heart is gradually hardened toward what you neglect and sensitized to whatever you set your affections on.

The simple truth is that you can't be tempted by what you don't think about (Heb. 11:15). As you neglect doubt and unbelief, your heart will begin to become insensitive to those things. Eventually, you can become hardened toward sin and failure.

4. How do the movies I watch, the music I listen to, and the books I read affect my heart?

A. Proverbs 4:23 in the *New Living Translation* says, **"Guard your heart above all else, for it determines the course of your life."** Notice that it isn't God's will for us, or our hopes, dreams, and desires, that determine the course of our lives; it's our hearts.

The average Christian today is watching the same television shows, reading the same books, and going to the same movies as the average unbeliever—and they are getting the exact same results in life. They are just as broke and sick as their unbelieving neighbors. If they put nothing but garbage into their hearts, they'll get nothing but garbage back out into their lives.

For instance, people come to me all the time wanting to be set free from struggles with sexual lust. Inevitably, as I talk to them, they reveal that they are focused on sex. Many times, they are into pornography, or they are exposing themselves to sexual content on the internet or in R-rated movies. Even when watching acceptable programs on television, the commercials will kill you. Sex is used to sell everything. Popular culture is bombarding society with sexual immorality. People cannot watch that stuff without being tempted by lustful thoughts. If they stop thinking about it, stop watching it, and stop focusing their attention on it, they won't be tempted.

We live in the world, but we don't have to be part of it (John 17:14). I'm not suggesting that we all move into monasteries or bury our heads in the sand. We are the salt of the earth, and to do any good, we have to get out of the saltshaker. The Lord doesn't want us to retreat from the world. On the contrary, we need to let our light illuminate the world. But I can also guarantee that God doesn't want us to be plugged into the world, taking in the same garbage as unbelievers.

5. Is God withholding His blessings from me until I put forth a good enough effort, or is something else keeping me from seeing His power manifest in my life?

A. The modern lifestyle of exposure to sin and carnality will harden your heart. It puts a layer of insensitivity between you and God. If you want your heart to be really sensitive to God, you have to reverse this process. You have to spend more time seeking God than you do plugging into the junk that this world has to offer. It's that simple.

A lot of people understand that God has better plans for their lives than they are experiencing. They know God wants them well, prospering, and living abundant lives. They have studied the Word, they go to church, and they know that an abundant life is out there waiting for them. Most people can see those blessings, but very few have sought God to the degree that their hearts are sensitive enough to receive those benefits.

God isn't withholding His blessings from you until you try hard enough. Your heart just isn't capable of receiving God's blessings when it is hardened toward Him. The solution is to focus your attention on God and harden your heart to the world.

6. I have a family to support, and a job that takes most of my time. How am I supposed to keep my responsibilities from overshadowing my relationship with God?

A. In the parable of the soils, Jesus described four heart conditions (Matt. 13:18-23 and Mark 4:14-20). The first heart condition doesn't understand the Word, and Satan steals it away before it can get rooted. The second heart condition receives the Word with joy, but quickly falls away when affliction and persecution come for the Word's sake. The third heart condition receives the Word, but it gets choked out before it can bear fruit. Jesus said of this third type of heart, **"The cares of this world, and the deceitfulness of riches, and the lusts of other things entering in, choke the word, and it becometh unfruitful"** (Mark 4:19).

When our hearts are focused on the cares of this life, the deceitfulness of riches, and the lust of other things, those distractions enter in and choke out the Word of God that has been planted in our hearts. For instance, we know that God wants to give us a life abundant with joy and peace, but many of us don't have joy or peace, because the cares of life, the deceitfulness of riches, and the desire for things are taking all of our time and attention. Our hearts have become hardened, and they aren't fully receiving the benefits of God's love.

Obviously, we need to earn a living and meet our responsibilities toward our families. But if we make our relationship with God a priority, then we will find time to meditate in the Word and spend time in God's presence. It may mean we have to give up a hobby or watching our favorite television show, but the benefits of relationship with God far outweigh anything we might sacrifice.

In order to experience the fullness of relationship with God, we have to change our focus. Jesus commanded us not to worry about the issues of this life, because He didn't want us to get distracted from what is really important: seeking the kingdom of God. To have hearts sensitive to God, we have to spend time meditating in His Word and considering the things of God. Our thoughts can't be dominated by the cares of this world and our senses. If we change the way we think and harden our hearts to the world, we will begin to experience the fullness of the abundant life that God desires for us. It's worth it.

Additional Resources:

1. *Hardness of Heart* is a four-part audio teaching available to listen to or download for free at www.awmi.net/extra/audio/1003.

2. *The Hardness of Heart*, a book by Andrew Wommack, deals with the crisis, the cause, and the cure for a hardened heart. It is available through bookstores or the AWM online store at www.awmi.net/store/usa/books/303.

3. *Lessons from David* is a four-part audio teaching that looks at the life of David, the only person the Lord called "a man after mine own heart," and makes direct applications to your life today. It is available to listen to or download for free at www.awmi.net/extra/audio/1041.

4. *How to Prepare Your Heart* is a three-part audio series that will teach you what the Bible says about setting your affections and how to do it. It is available to listen to or download for free at www.awmi.net/extra/audio/1010.

Self-Centeredness: The Source of All Grief
Lesson 16

Whosoever will come after me, let him deny himself, and take up his cross, and follow me.

MARK 8:34

"A cross is something you die on. To 'take up' our cross means that we are supposed to die to ourselves and follow Jesus" (Sharper than a Two-Edged Sword, Chapter 16).

1. **How is pride related to strife in my life?**

   A. Whether you realize it or not, your self-centeredness is the root of all your grief. The book of Proverbs says, **"Only by pride cometh contention: but with the well advised is wisdom"** (Prov. 13:10). It doesn't say pride is "one of" the leading causes of conflict or that it is more common for certain personality types; it says that pride is the *only* reason for contention. There is no other source, no other reason, and no other explanation for contention other than pride. And contention is the beginning of strife: **"The beginning of strife is as when one letteth out water: therefore leave off contention, before it be meddled with"** (Prov. 17:14).

   You don't just jump from having a life filled with love and harmony into strife all at once. It's a progressive process, and the first step is contention. Pride and self-centeredness lead to contention, which opens the door to strife. You might think you get angry because of the things other people say and do to you. You don't think of yourself as being the source of the strife in your life, but you are. What other people do doesn't cause disharmony—your own self-centeredness does, and pride is the root of it all.

2. **How can I be the one making myself angry when it's the things other people are doing to me that make me mad?**

   A. The things people say and do to us aren't really what cause us to be angry and bitter; it's our pride and self-focus that make us *react* to what they have done. Jesus said, **"Whosoever will come after me, let him deny himself, and take up his cross, and follow me"** (Mark 8:34). A cross is something we die on. To **"take up"** our crosses means that we are supposed to die to ourselves and follow Jesus.

The reason it hurts so much when people insult or criticize us is because we aren't dead to ourselves. We brood over insults and fan the flames until we see the people who come against as having inflicted a huge injustice upon us. No one enjoys suffering wrong, but it's really our own pride that causes us to feel so hurt. If we are dead to ourselves, people can insult us all they want, and it won't bother us one bit. We can go down to the morgue, pull out a corpse, and spit on, insult, or assault it all we want—it isn't going to respond. Dead people don't take offense.

Total selflessness is a level of perfection that isn't achievable in this life, but we can start heading in that direction. I haven't arrived at selflessness, but I've left.

3. Proud people are always bragging about how great they are. Is it really possible for a shy person to be full of pride?

A. Arrogance is only one manifestation of pride. Exalting yourself is one way that pride shows itself, but timidity and low self-esteem are also pride rearing its ugly head. They are opposite behaviors, but the source of both is the same. Just like a stick has two ends, arrogance and timidity are opposite ends of the same issue. Pride, at its root, is just self-centeredness, and whether you are conceited or cower from attention, the root cause is pride. It doesn't matter whether you think you are better than everybody else or if you think you are a nobody, both attitudes are self-centered.

I can say this with great conviction because I was an extreme introvert when I was a teenager. I couldn't even look a person in the face and talk to them. I was painfully shy. Some people might say, "Well, that was just your personality type." No, it was self-centeredness. Shyness, or timidity, is extreme self-centeredness—it's just a different manifestation of pride than arrogance is. I can tell you what I was thinking that caused me to be timid: I was always thinking about me and what other people thought about me. I was so afraid of other peoples' criticism that I wouldn't open up and talk to people. I was afraid I might say something that would make me sound dumb.

4. What is real humility?

A. Moses is a striking example of biblical humility. He wrote, **"Now the man Moses was very meek, above all the men which were upon the face of the earth"** (Num. 12:3). Moses led three million Jews out of Egypt, so there must have been several million people on earth at the time. Moses was the meekest of them all. What is even more striking is that Moses wrote this statement about himself. We have been taught a religious concept of humility that says we should knock ourselves down and have a low sense of self-worth, but that isn't humility. By that way of thinking, Moses couldn't have written that he was the meekest man on earth and still have been meek.

True humility means you don't have an agenda of self-promotion. You don't exalt yourself or debase yourself, because you aren't focused on "self." A humble person isn't concerned about the opinions of other people. God inspired Moses to write that he was the meekest person on the planet, and he did it because he wasn't self-focused. Not being self-centered, he could express the truth without falling into the trap of exalting himself.

5. What does God's kind of love look like?

A. In a well-known passage of Scripture about love, the Apostle Paul wrote,

> **Love endures long and is patient and kind; love never is envious nor boils over with jealousy, is not boastful or vainglorious, does not display itself haughtily. It is not conceited (arrogant and inflated with pride); it is not rude (unmannerly) and does not act unbecomingly. Love (God's love in us) does not insist on its own rights or its own way, for it is not self-seeking; it is not touchy or fretful or resentful; it takes no account of the evil done to it [it pays no attention to a suffered wrong].**

> **1 CORINTHIANS 13:4-5**
> **AMPLIFIED BIBLE, CLASSIC EDITION**

God's kind of love doesn't even notice a wrong suffered. When we are thinking more about the other person than we are about ourselves, we won't be hurt. We won't take things to heart the way most people do.

Jesus showed us a model of putting others before ourselves. While He was on the cross, Jesus asked the Father to forgive those who crucified Him. He was more concerned for them than He was focused on His own situation. This attitude is outside of the norm, but the Bible says that the works Jesus did, we should do also (John 14:12). So, we should be imitating Jesus' self*less*ness instead of embracing a culture of self-centeredness.

6. How will being selfless positively impact my life? Is it worth my effort?

A. We can't control how other people treat us, but we can control ourselves Self-centeredness is the source of grief in our lives, and the Word of God says that if we want to be free from strife and bitterness, we need to die to ourselves and follow Jesus. We need to put our focus on God and love God more than we love ourselves. Once we love God and receive His love for us, the selfless love that Jesus expressed will flow through us toward other people. We'll see a difference in our attitude. We should seek God first and love other people more than ourselves. As we do, the hurt and pain in our lives will begin to evaporate.

Additional Resources:

1. *Self-Centeredness: The Source of All Grief* is an audio teaching available to listen to or download for free at www.awmi.net/extra/audio/1001.

2. *Self-Centeredness: The Source of All Grief* is a booklet by Andrew Wommack that discusses how difficult situations have a way of revealing the heart, and how love, joy, and peace can be yours—even in the worst of situations. It is available through the AWM online store at www.awmi.net/store/usa/books/315.

3. The *Christian Survival Kit* is a sixteen-part audio teaching that details how Jesus' instructions to His disciples the night before His crucifixion told them what they needed to know to keep them from being overcome with grief during that trying time. It is available to listen to or download for free at www.awmi.net/extra/audio/1001.

4. *Lessons from Elijah* is a five-part audio teaching that covers the scriptural example that Elijah provides—both good and bad. It is available to listen to or download for free at www.awmi.net/extra/audio/1026.

5. *How to Deal with Grief* is a four-part audio teaching. Grief is something that each one of us encounters sooner or later. It cannot be avoided, but it can be dealt with in a positive way. This teaching will show you how. It is available to listen to or download for free at www.awmi.net/extra/audio/1032.

6. *God's Kind of Love to You* is a five-part audio teaching that shows how our heavenly Father is a God of love. It is available to listen to or download for free at www.awmi.net/extra/audio/1054.

About the Author

For over four decades, Andrew Wommack has traveled America and the world teaching the truth of the Gospel. His profound revelation of the Word of God is taught with clarity and simplicity, emphasizing God's unconditional love and the balance between grace and faith. He reaches millions of people through the daily *Gospel Truth* radio and television programs, broadcast both domestically and internationally. He founded Charis Bible College in 1994 and has since established Charis Bible College extension schools in other major cities of America and around the world. Andrew has produced a library of teaching materials, available in print, audio, and visual formats. And, as it has been from the beginning, his ministry continues to distribute free audio materials to those who cannot afford them.

Receive Jesus as Your Savior

Choosing to receive Jesus Christ as your Lord and Savior is the most important decision you'll ever make!

God's Word promises, **"That if thou shalt confess with thy mouth the Lord Jesus, and shalt believe in thine heart that God hath raised him from the dead, thou shalt be saved. For with the heart man believeth unto righteousness; and with the mouth confession is made unto salvation"** (Rom. 10:9-10). **"For whosoever shall call upon the name of the Lord shall be saved"** (Rom. 10:13).

By His grace, God has already done everything to provide salvation. Your part is simply to believe and receive.

Pray out loud, *"Jesus, I confess that You are my Lord and Savior. I believe in my heart that God raised You from the dead. By faith in Your Word, I receive salvation now. Thank You for saving me!"*

The very moment you commit your life to Jesus Christ, the truth of His Word instantly comes to pass in your spirit. Now that you're born again, there's a brand-new you!

Please contact me and let me know that you've prayed to receive Jesus as your Savior. I would like to rejoice with you and help you understand more fully what has taken place in your life. I'll send you a free gift that will help you understand and grow in your new relationship with the Lord. *Welcome to your new life!*

Receive the Holy Spirit

As His child, your loving heavenly Father wants to give you the supernatural power you need to live this new life.

"For every one that asketh receiveth; and he that seeketh findeth; and to him that knocketh it shall be opened...how much more shall your heavenly Father give the Holy Spirit to them that ask him?" (Luke 11:10 and 13).

All you have to do is ask, believe, and receive!

Pray, *"Father, I recognize my need for Your power to live this new life. Please fill me with Your Holy Spirit. By faith, I receive it right now! Thank You for baptizing me. Holy Spirit, You are welcome in my life!"*

Congratulations—now you're filled with God's supernatural power!

Some syllables from a language you don't recognize will rise up from your heart to your mouth (1 Cor. 14:14). As you speak them out loud by faith, you're releasing God's power from within and building yourself up in your spirit (1 Cor. 14:4). You can do this whenever and wherever you like.

It doesn't really matter whether you felt anything or not when you prayed to receive the Lord and His Spirit. If you believed in your heart that you received, then God's Word promises that you did. **"Therefore I say unto you, What things soever ye desire, when ye pray, believe that ye receive them, and ye shall have them"** (Mark 11:24). God always honors His Word—believe it!

Please contact me and let me know that you've prayed to receive Jesus as your Savior or to be filled with the Holy Spirit. I would like to rejoice with you and help you understand more fully what has taken place in your life. I'll send you a free gift that will help you understand and grow in your new relationship with the Lord. *Welcome to your new life!*